LEGAL RESEARCH EXERCISES

Following The Bluebook: A Uniform System of Citation

Eighth Edition

By

Nancy P. Johnson
Law Librarian and Professor of Law
Georgia State University
College of Law Library

Susan T. Phillips
Director of the Law Library and Professor of Law
Texas Wesleyan University
School of Law Library

To Accompany

Berring & Edinger's

FINDING THE LAW

and

Cohen, Berring and Olson's

HOW TO FIND THE LAW

THOMSC
★
WEST

D1318886

Mat #40129621

COPYRIGHT © 2003 By WEST GROUP
                610 Opperman Drive
                P.O. Box 64526
                St. Paul, MN 55164–0526
                1–800–328–9352

ISBN 0–314–14544–3

TEXT IS PRINTED ON 10% POST CONSUMER RECYCLED PAPER

TABLE OF CONTENTS

Student's Introduction

Assignment:

STUDENT'S INTRODUCTION

Mastering efficient research skills is more important than ever in the current legal environment. This eighth edition of *Legal Research Exercises, Following The Bluebook: A Uniform System of Citation* will help you learn to master efficient legal research skills. In completing the assignments in this book, you should become familiar with many kinds of research materials and you can use this familiarity to formulate basic research strategy. You will develop skills in using your law library and you will feel more comfortable with legal citation form.

We intend that none of the questions in this book to be extremely time-consuming. If you cannot find an answer, ask your instructor for help. Read the relevant material in your legal research text before attempting to complete the assignments. When we ask for a full citation, we want you to include the case name, reporter citation, court (if necessary) and a year in your citation, as specified by *The Bluebook: A Uniform System of Citation* (17th ed.)

Each assignment contains four variations (A, B, C, D). Since the questions are identical for the four variations, you will work on one variation. Some assignments relate to each other. For example, you Shepardize the same case that you worked with in the previous assignment; therefore, you should use the same variation throughout all assignments.

Practice professionalism by reshelving your books once you answer the questions. It takes only a few seconds to reshelve the materials.

We have tried very hard to eliminate all errors, but we apologize for any that you may discover. We have learned that no matter how painstaking our efforts are in this regard, because of the republishing of legal materials, errors creep into a book of this nature as time passes. Please contact your instructors when you discover a problem. For a list of corrections, please see the information at the *Finding the Law* website at: http://www.law.berkeley.edu/faculty/berringr/findingthelaw/index.html.

Nancy Johnson gratefully acknowledges her colleagues and law students at Georgia State University College of Law who have helped enhanced these assignments during the various editions. Nancy would like to thank her research assistant Beth Howard for her fine work. Nancy would also like to thank her family for their understanding during the completion of yet another edition. Susan Phillips would like to thank Karin Strohbeck for her work on this edition, Anna Teller, Wendy Law, Joan Stringfellow and the library staff at Texas Wesleyan University Law Library. Susan also extends here gratitude to her entire family, including mother Marty, husband Michael and daughters Kyle and Jillian, for their continued support during the writing process.

ASSIGNMENT ONE
FINDING AND CITING CASES
EXERCISE A

GOALS OF THIS ASSIGNMENT:
To teach you how to find cases when you have citations.
To acquaint you with the location of reporters in your law library.
To familiarize you with the rules for citing cases in *The Bluebook: A Uniform System of Citation*, 17th ed.

CITATION RULES: Read I.2-I.4(a), P.1(a), P.3, Rules 6.1(a), 10.2.1, 10.2.2, 10.3.1, 10.3.2, 10.4, 10.5 and refer to Tables 1, 6, and 11 of *The Bluebook*. Apply these rules as you learn the correct citation for each case.
Throughout this book, when we ask that you provide a full citation, give the name, citation and date of the case, and any other necessary information (such as court) required by *The Bluebook*.

The first two questions introduce you to the rules for citing U.S. Supreme Court cases. **Example: *Loving v. Virginia*, 388 U.S. 1 (1967).**

United States Reports, abbreviated U.S. in case citation, is the official reporter. Note that no parallel, unofficial reporters are listed for U.S. Supreme Court Cases when a U.S. citation is available. At the beginning of T.1 in *The Bluebook*, read the instructions for the **Supreme Court**.

1.   If an opinion of the U.S. Supreme Court has not yet been published in *United States Reports*, which unofficial reporters should you cite instead, in order of preference?

2.   State the full citation for 528 U.S. 440.

The third question requires you to find and cite a U.S. Supreme Court case from before 1875. They published these cases in reporters known as **nominative** reporters, because they were generally known by the name of the person who compiled the volume. The form of citation for a case in a nominative reporter differs from the form for a case appearing in contemporary sources. Study the rules for citing cases found in nominative reporters (*The Bluebook* calls them "early American reporters" see Rule 10.3.2.). Here is an example of how to cite a U.S. Supreme Court nominative reporter: ***Hughes v. Union Ins. Co.*, 21 U.S. (8 Wheat.) 294 (1823).**

3.   State the full citation for 77 U.S. 158. Note: For the date, use the year of the Court Term.

Next, you must find and cite a federal court of appeals case from a circuit. When citing a court of appeals case always list the circuit within the parentheses, along with the date. **Example:** *Bonilla v. Volvo Car Corp.*, **150 F.3d 62 (1ˢᵗ Cir. 1998).**

4.   State the full citation for 285 F.3d 445.

Now, find and cite a federal district court case. When citing a case from district court, the particular court is included within the parentheses. **Example:** *Hillard v. Guidant Corp.*, **76 F. Supp. 2d 566 (M.D. Pa. 1999).**

5.   State the full citation for 226 F. Supp. 2d 233. Note: The district is listed before the state--the division, if listed, is listed after. Always include the district in the citation, never the division.

In general, for state decisions the state and the name of the court should be included within the parentheses. However, do not include the name of the court if the court of decision is the highest court of the state. Here is an example of how to cite a Pennsylvania Supreme Court case. How do you know what to include in the parentheses? Read Rules 10.4(b) and look at the listing for Pennsylvania in T.1. **Example:** *Commonwealth v. Brayboy*, **246 A.2d 675 (Pa. 1968).**

Find 51 P.3d 874 to answer Questions 6 and 7.

6.   State the full citation for 51 P.3d 874.

Should you ever cite the official version of a case? Yes, if the case is very old and there is no regional citation. Otherwise, you should cite it **only** if you are **including it in a document submitted to a state court whose local rules require citation to the official reporter.** (See Rule 10.3.1(a) and P.3.) Here is our previous example cited in such a context. **Example:** *Commonwealth v. Brayboy,* **431 Pa. 365, 246 A.2d 675 (1968).** Note: We followed Rule 10.4(b) and omitted the jurisdiction Pa. from the parentheses because it is unambiguously conveyed by the reporter title.

7.   State the full citation for 51 P.3d 874, assuming you are including this citation in a document submitted to a California state court whose local rules require citing to the official report volume.

Next, find an opinion from a state intermediate appellate court and cite it correctly. **Example:** *Maluszewski v. Allstate Ins. Co.,* **640 A.2d 129 (Conn. App. Ct. 1994).**

Find 87 S.W.3d 797 to answer Questions 8 and 9.

8.   State the full citation for 87 S.W.3d 797.

Our previous example of an intermediate state appellate court citation cited in a document submitted to a Connecticut state court whose local rules require citing to the official report volume would look like this. **Example:** *Maluszewski v. Allstate Ins. Co.,* **34 Conn. App. 27, 540 A.2d 129 (1994).**

9.   State the full citation for 87 S.W.3d 797, assuming you are including this citation in a document to an Arkansas state court whose local rules require citing to the official report volume.

A good place to review legal citation form in briefs and memoranda is *Introduction to Basic Legal Citation* (2002-2003 ed.) by Peter W. Martin at http://www.law.cornell.edu/citation.

ASSIGNMENT ONE
FINDING AND CITING CASES
EXERCISE B

GOALS OF THIS ASSIGNMENT:
To teach you how to find cases when you have citations.
To acquaint you with the location of reporters in your law library.
To familiarize you with the rules for citing cases in *The Bluebook: A Uniform System of Citation*, 17th ed.

CITATION RULES: Read I.2-I.4(a), P.1(a), P.3, Rules 6.1(a), 10.2.1, 10.2.2, 10.3.1, 10.3.2, 10.4, 10.5 and refer to Tables 1, 6, and 11 of *The Bluebook.* Apply these rules as you learn the correct citation for each case.
Throughout this book, when we ask that you provide a full citation, give the name, citation and date of the case, and any other necessary information (such as court) required by *The Bluebook*.

The first two questions introduce you to the rules for citing U.S. Supreme Court cases. **Example: *Loving v. Virginia,* 388 U.S. 1 (1967).**

United States Reports, abbreviated U.S. in case citation, is the official reporter. Note that no parallel, unofficial reporters are listed for U.S. Supreme Court Cases when a U.S. citation is available. At the beginning of T.1 in *The Bluebook*, read the instructions for the **Supreme Court**.

1.   If an opinion of the U.S. Supreme Court has not yet been published in *United States Reports*, which unofficial reporters should you cite instead, in order of preference?

2.   State the full citation for 529 U.S. 460.

The third question requires you to find and cite a U.S. Supreme Court case from before 1875. They published these cases in reporters known as **nominative** reporters, because they were generally known by the name of the person who compiled the volume. The form of citation for a case in a nominative reporter differs from the form for a case appearing in contemporary sources. Study the rules for citing cases found in nominative reporters (*The Bluebook* calls them "early American reporters" see Rule 10.3.2.). Here is an example of how to cite a U.S. Supreme Court nominative reporter: ***Hughes v. Union Ins. Co.,* 21 U.S. (8 Wheat.) 294 (1823).**

3. State the full citation for 62 U.S. 294. Note: For the date, use the year of the Court Term.

    Next, you must find and cite a federal court of appeals case from a circuit. When citing a court of appeals case always list the circuit within the parentheses, along with the date. **Example: *Bonilla v. Volvo Car Corp.*, 150 F.3d 62 (1ˢᵗ Cir. 1998).**

4. State the full citation for 311 F.3d 993.

    Now, find and cite a federal district court case. When citing a case from district court, the particular court is included within the parentheses. **Example: *Hillard v. Guidant Corp.*, 76 F. Supp. 2d 566 (M.D. Pa. 1999).**

5. State the full citation for 220 F. Supp. 2d 26. Note: The district is listed before the state—the division, if listed, is listed after. Always include the district in the citation, never the division.

    In general, for state decisions the state and the name of the court should be included within the parentheses. However, do not include the name of the court if the court of decision is the highest court of the state. Here is an example of how to cite a Pennsylvania Supreme Court case. How do you know what to include in the parentheses? Read Rules 10.4(b) and look at the listing for Pennsylvania in T.1. **Example: *Commonwealth v. Brayboy*, 246 A.2d 675 (Pa. 1968).**

    Find 571 S.E.2d 770 to answer Questions 6 and 7.

6. State the full citation for 571 S.E.2d 770.

Should you ever cite the official version of a case? Yes, if the case is very old and there is no regional citation. Otherwise, you should cite it **only** if you are **including it in a document submitted to a state court whose local rules require citation to the official reporter.** (See Rule 10.3.1(a) and P.3.) Here is our previous example cited in such a context. **Example: *Commonwealth v. Brayboy,* 431 Pa. 365, 246 A.2d 675 (1968).** Note: We followed Rule 10.4(b) and omitted the jurisdiction Pa. from the parentheses because it is unambiguously conveyed by the reporter title.

7. State the full citation for 571 S.E.2d 770, assuming you are including this citation in a document submitted to a Georgia state court whose local rules require citing to the official report volume.

Next, find an opinion from a state intermediate appellate court and cite it correctly. **Example: *Maluszewski v. Allstate Ins. Co.,* 640 A.2d 129 (Conn. App. Ct. 1994).**

Find 56 P.3d 504 to answer Questions 8 and 9.

8. State the full citation for 56 P.3d 504.

Our previous example of an intermediate state appellate court citation cited in a document submitted to a Connecticut state court whose local rules require citing to the official report volume would look like this. **Example: *Maluszewski v. Allstate Ins. Co.,* 34 Conn. App. 27, 540 A.2d 129 (1994).**

9. State the full citation for 56 P.3d 504, assuming you are including this citation in a document to an Oregon state court whose local rules require citing to the official report volume.

A good place to review legal citation form in briefs and memoranda is *Introduction to Basic Legal Citation* (2002-2003 ed.) by Peter W. Martin at http://www.law.cornell.edu/citation.

ASSIGNMENT ONE
FINDING AND CITING CASES
EXERCISE C

GOALS OF THIS ASSIGNMENT:
To teach you how to find cases when you have citations.
To acquaint you with the location of reporters in your law library.
To familiarize you with the rules for citing cases in *The Bluebook: A Uniform System of Citation*, 17th ed.

CITATION RULES: Read I.2-I.4(a), P.1(a), P.3, Rules 6.1(a), 10.2.1, 10.2.2, 10.3.1, 10.3.2, 10.4, 10.5 and refer to Tables 1, 6, and 11 of *The Bluebook*. Apply these rules as you learn the correct citation for each case.
Throughout this book, when we ask that you provide a full citation, give the name, citation and date of the case, and any other necessary information (such as court) required by *The Bluebook*.

The first two questions introduce you to the rules for citing U.S. Supreme Court cases. **Example: *Loving v. Virginia*, 388 U.S. 1 (1967).**

United States Reports, abbreviated U.S. in case citation, is the official reporter. Note that no parallel, unofficial reporters are listed for U.S. Supreme Court Cases when a U.S. citation is available. At the beginning of T.1 in *The Bluebook*, read the instructions for the **Supreme Court**.

1.   If an opinion of the U.S. Supreme Court has not yet been published in *United States Reports*, which unofficial reporters should you cite instead, in order of preference?

2.   State the full citation for 530 U.S. 211.

The third question requires you to find and cite a U.S. Supreme Court case from before 1875. They published these cases in reporters known as **nominative** reporters, because they were generally known by the name of the person who compiled the volume. The form of citation for a case in a nominative reporter differs from the form for a case appearing in contemporary sources. Study the rules for citing cases found in nominative reporters (*The Bluebook* calls them "early American reporters" see Rule 10.3.2.). Here is an example of how to cite a U.S. Supreme Court nominative reporter: ***Hughes v. Union Ins. Co.*, 21 U.S. (8 Wheat.) 294 (1823).**

3.   State the full citation for 33 U.S. 112. Note: For the date, use the year of the Court Term.

Next, you must find and cite a federal court of appeals case from a circuit. When citing a court of appeals case always list the circuit within the parentheses, along with the date. **Example: *Bonilla v. Volvo Car Corp.*, 150 F.3d 62 (1ˢᵗ Cir. 1998).**

4.   State the full citation for 302 F.3d 98.

Now, find and cite a federal district court case. When citing a case from district court, the particular court is included within the parentheses. **Example: *Hillard v. Guidant Corp.*, 76 F. Supp. 2d 566 (M.D. Pa. 1999).**

5.   State the full citation for 216 F. Supp. 2d 1299. Note: The district is listed before the state—the division, if listed, is listed after. Always include the district in the citation, never the division.

In general, for state decisions the state and the name of the court should be included within the parentheses. However, do not include the name of the court if the court of decision is the highest court of the state. Here is an example of how to cite a Pennsylvania Supreme Court case. How do you know what to include in the parentheses? Read Rules 10.4(b) and look at the listing for Pennsylvania in T.1. **Example: *Commonwealth v. Brayboy*, 246 A.2d 675 (Pa. 1968).**

Find 777 N.E.2d 1238 to answer Questions 6 and 7.

6.   State the full citation for 777 N.E.2d 1238.

Should you ever cite the official version of a case? Yes, if the case is very old and there is no regional citation. Otherwise, you should cite it **only** if you are **including it in a document submitted to a state court whose local rules require citation to the official reporter.** (See Rule 10.3.1(a) and P.3.) Here is our previous example cited in such a context. **Example:** *Commonwealth v. Brayboy,* **431 Pa. 365, 246 A.2d 675 (1968).** Note: We followed Rule 10.4(b) and omitted the jurisdiction Pa. from the parentheses because it is unambiguously conveyed by the reporter title.

7. State the full citation for 777 N.E.2d 1238, assuming you are including this citation in a document submitted to a Massachusetts state court whose local rules require citing to the official report volume.

Next, find an opinion from a state intermediate appellate court and cite it correctly. **Example:** *Maluszewski v. Allstate Ins. Co.,* **640 A.2d 129 (Conn. App. Ct. 1994).**

Find 649 N.W.2d 197 to answer Questions 8 and 9.

8. State the full citation for 649 N.W.2d 197.

Our previous example of an intermediate state appellate court citation cited in a document submitted to a Connecticut state court whose local rules require citing to the official report volume would look like this. **Example:** *Maluszewski v. Allstate Ins. Co.,* **34 Conn. App. 27, 540 A.2d 129 (1994).**

9. State the full citation for 649 N.W.2d 197, assuming you are including this citation in a document to a Nebraska state court whose local rules require citing to the official report volume.

A good place to review legal citation form in briefs and memoranda is *Introduction to Basic Legal Citation* (2002-2003 ed.) by Peter W. Martin at http://www.law.cornell.edu/citation.

ASSIGNMENT ONE
FINDING AND CITING CASES
EXERCISE D

GOALS OF THIS ASSIGNMENT:
To teach you how to find cases when you have citations.
To acquaint you with the location of reporters in your law library.
To familiarize you with the rules for citing cases in *The Bluebook: A Uniform System of Citation*, **17th ed.**

CITATION RULES: Read I.2-I.4(a), P.1(a), P.3, Rules 6.1(a), 10.2.1, 10.2.2, 10.3.1, 10.3.2, 10.4, 10.5 and refer to Tables 1, 6, and 11 of *The Bluebook*. Apply these rules as you learn the correct citation for each case.
Throughout this book, when we ask that you provide a full citation, give the name, citation and date of the case, and any other necessary information (such as court) required by *The Bluebook*.

The first two questions introduce you to the rules for citing U.S. Supreme Court cases. **Example:** *Loving v. Virginia*, **388 U.S. 1 (1967).**

United States Reports, abbreviated U.S. in case citation, is the official reporter. Note that no parallel, unofficial reporters are listed for U.S. Supreme Court Cases when a U.S. citation is available. At the beginning of T.1 in *The Bluebook*, read the instructions for the **Supreme Court**.

1.   If an opinion of the U.S. Supreme Court has not yet been published in *United States Reports*, which unofficial reporters should you cite instead, in order of preference?

2.   State the full citation for 531 U.S. 533.

The third question requires you to find and cite a U.S. Supreme Court case from before 1875. They published these cases in reporters known as **nominative** reporters, because they were generally known by the name of the person who compiled the volume. The form of citation for a case in a nominative reporter differs from the form for a case appearing in contemporary sources. Study the rules for citing cases found in nominative reporters (*The Bluebook* calls them "early American reporters" see Rule 10.3.2.). Here is an example of how to cite a U.S. Supreme Court nominative reporter: *Hughes v. Union Ins. Co.*, **21 U.S. (8 Wheat.) 294 (1823).**

3. State the full citation for 82 U.S. 450. Note: For the date, use the year of the Court Term.

Next, you must find and cite a federal court of appeals case from a circuit. When citing a court of appeals case always list the circuit within the parentheses, along with the date. **Example: *Bonilla v. Volvo Car Corp.*, 150 F.3d 62 (1ˢᵗ Cir. 1998).**

4. State the full citation for 294 F.3d 830.

Now, find and cite a federal district court case. When citing a case from district court, the particular court is included within the parentheses. **Example: *Hillard v. Guidant Corp.*, 76 F. Supp. 2d 566 (M.D. Pa. 1999).**

5. State the full citation for 198 F. Supp. 2d 997. Note: The district is listed before the state—the division, if listed, is listed after. Always include the district in the citation, never the division.

In general, for state decisions the state and the name of the court should be included within the parentheses. However, do not include the name of the court if the court of decision is the highest court of the state. Here is an example of how to cite a Pennsylvania Supreme Court case. How do you know what to include in the parentheses? Read Rules 10.4(b) and look at the listing for Pennsylvania in T.1. **Example: *Commonwealth v. Brayboy*, 246 A.2d 675 (Pa. 1968).**

Find 807 A.2d 13 to answer Questions 6 and 7.

6. State the full citation for 807 A.2d 13.

Should you ever cite the official version of a case? Yes, if the case is very old and there is no regional citation. Otherwise, you should cite it **only** if you are **including it in a document submitted to a state court whose local rules require citation to the official reporter.** (See Rule 10.3.1(a) and P.3.) Here is our previous example cited in such a context. **Example: *Commonwealth v. Brayboy,* 431 Pa. 365, 246 A.2d 675 (1968).** Note: We followed Rule 10.4(b) and omitted the jurisdiction Pa. from the parentheses because it is unambiguously conveyed by the reporter title.

7. State the full citation for 807 A.2d 13, assuming you are including this citation in a document submitted to a Maryland state court whose local rules require citing to the official report volume.

Next, find an opinion from a state intermediate appellate court and cite it correctly. **Example: *Maluszewski v. Allstate Ins. Co.*, 640 A.2d 129 (Conn. App. Ct. 1994).**

Find 562 S.E.2d 794 to answer Questions 8 and 9.

8. State the full citation for 562 S.E.2d 794.

Our previous example of an intermediate state appellate court citation cited in a document submitted to a Connecticut state court whose local rules require citing to the official report volume would look like this. **Example: *Maluszewski v. Allstate Ins. Co.*, 34 Conn. App. 27, 540 A.2d 129 (1994).**

9. State the full citation for 562 S.E.2d 794, assuming you are including this citation in a document to a Georgia state court whose local rules require citing to the official report volume.

A good place to review legal citation form in briefs and memoranda is *Introduction to Basic Legal Citation* (2002-2003 ed.) by Peter W. Martin at http://www.law.cornell.edu/citation.

GOALS OF THIS ASSIGNMENT:
To familiarize you with the parts of a case in three different reporters.
To introduce you to star paging.

CITATION RULES: Use *The Bluebook: A Uniform System of Citation*, 17th ed., Rules 10.2, 10.2.1, 10.2.2, 10.3, 10.4, 10.5 and Tables 1, 6 and 11. Use the format for court documents and legal memoranda and assume that the case citation appears in a citation sentence.

Locate 527 U.S. 150 to answer Questions 1-9.

1.   Find 527 U.S. 150. This is the official reporter version of the case. What is the case name? Use correct form (Rule 10.2).

2.   On what date was the case decided?

3.   What is the docket number of the case?

4.   Which party is the respondent?

5.   Which Justice wrote the majority opinion?

6.   Which Justice wrote the dissenting opinion?

7. What was the lower court cite of this case, on its way up to the Supreme Court? Note: You are looking for the cite of a F.3d case.

8. How did the Supreme Court act on the judgment of the court below?

9. Who argued the cause for the petitioner?

To answer Questions 10-17 you will need to compare the case from Question 1 in the two unofficial versions, S. Ct., L. Ed., of this opinion.

10. Find the appropriate book of vol. 119 of the *Supreme Court Reporter* (S. Ct.), published by West, and vol. 144 of the *U.S. Supreme Court Reports--Lawyers' Edition* (L. Ed. 2d), published by LexisNexis. These two reporters are unofficial reporters for United States Supreme Court cases. Use the Cases Reported table at the front of S. Ct. and the Table of Cases Reported in the front of L. Ed. to find your case in both reporters.

    a. What is the S. Ct. cite?

    b. What is the L. Ed. cite?

11. Examine the headnotes preceding the opinions. On which page of which reporter does the second West topic and key number appear? (Note: A small key-shaped symbol accompanies the West topic and key number.)

12.   State the West topic and key number from the preceding question.

13.   Each headnote corresponds to a particular part of the Court's opinion. Examine the opinion in S. Ct. and look for references to the headnote numbers (boldface numbers in brackets **[1]**). On which page of the S. Ct. **opinion** is there a reference to the second West headnote?

14.   Star paging enables attorneys using L. Ed. or S. Ct. to cite U.S. paging without having U.S. itself. Star paging in L. Ed. is shown thus: **[405 US 729]**. Star paging in S. Ct. is indicated thus: ⊥**729**. Looking at the *Supreme Court Reporter* and using star paging ⊥, state on which page of *United States Reports* (U.S.) you will find the corresponding material related to the second **[2]** West headnote.

15.   Notice that the two unofficial reporters have different headnotes. How many headnotes are in the *U.S. Supreme Court Reports, Lawyers' Edition*?

16.   Question 8 asked you about the **disposition** of the case, that is, how the Supreme Court treated the judgment of the court below. The **holding** is another part of a case, the application of rules of law to the specific key facts in the case. What is the holding of this case as to what the Federal Circuit must use when reviewing Patent and Trademark Office (PTO) findings of fact? You may want to review the syllabus of the case.

17.   In what title of the United States Code (U.S.C.) is the federal Administrative Procedure Act located?

ASSIGNMENT TWO
SUPREME COURT REPORTERS AND PARTS OF A CASE
EXERCISE B

GOALS OF THIS ASSIGNMENT:
To familiarize you with the parts of a case in three different reporters.
To introduce you to star paging.

CITATION RULES: Use *The Bluebook: A Uniform System of Citation*, 17th ed., Rules 10.2, 10.2.1, 10.2.2, 10.3, 10.4, 10.5 and Tables 1, 6 and 11. Use the format for court documents and legal memoranda and assume that the case citation appears in a citation sentence.

Locate 519 U.S. 234 to answer Questions 1-9.

1.   Find 519 U.S. 234. This is the official reporter version of the case. What is the case name? Use correct form (Rule 10.2).

2.   On what date was the case decided?

3.   What is the docket number of the case?

4.   Which party is the respondent?

5.   Which Justice wrote the opinion of the court?

6.   Which Justice wrote a dissenting opinion?

7. What was the lower court cite of this case, on its way up to the Supreme Court? Note: You are looking for the cite of a F.3d case.

8. How did the Supreme Court act on the judgment of the court below?

9. Who argued the cause for the petitioners?

To answer Questions 10-17, you will need to compare the case from Question 1 in the two unofficial versions, S. Ct., L. Ed., of this opinion.

10. Find the appropriate book of vol. 117 of the *Supreme Court Reporter* (S. Ct.), published by West, and vol. 136 of the *U.S. Supreme Court Reports—Lawyers' Edition* (L. Ed. 2d), published then by Lexis Publishing and now by LexisNexis. These two reporters are unofficial reporters for United States Supreme Court cases. Use the Cases Reported table at the front of S. Ct. and the Table of Cases Reported in the front of L. Ed. to find your case in both reporters.

    a. What is the S. Ct. cite?

    b. What is the L. Ed. cite?

11. Examine the headnotes preceding the opinions. On what page of which reporter does the fifth West topic and key number appear? (Note: A small key-shaped symbol accompanies the West topic and key number.)

12.   State the West topic and key number from the preceding question.

13.   Each headnote corresponds to a particular part of the Court's opinion. Examine the opinion in S. Ct. and look for references to the headnote numbers (boldface numbers in brackets **[1]**). On what page of the S. Ct. **opinion** is there a reference to the fifth West headnote?

14.   Star paging enables attorneys using L. Ed. or S. Ct. to cite U.S. paging without using U.S. itself. Star paging in L. Ed. is shown thus: **[405 US 729]**. Star paging in S. Ct. is indicated thus: ⊥**729.** Looking at the *Supreme Court Reporter* and using star paging ⊥, state the page of *United States Reports* (U.S.) on which the corresponding material related to the fifth **[5]** West headnote begins.

15.   Notice that the two unofficial reporters have different headnotes. How many headnotes are in the *U.S. Supreme Court Reports, Lawyers' Edition*?

16.   Question 8 asked you about the **disposition** of the case, that is, how the Supreme Court treated the judgment of the court below. The **holding** is another part of a case, the application of rules of law to the specific key facts in the case. What is the holding of this case as to whether the amended version of § 207 of the Indian Land Consolidation Act render the provision constitutional? You may want to review the syllabus of the case.

17.   In what title of the United States Code (U.S.C.) is the Indian Land Consolidation Act located?

ASSIGNMENT TWO
SUPREME COURT REPORTERS AND PARTS OF A CASE
EXERCISE C

GOALS OF THIS ASSIGNMENT:
To familiarize you with the parts of a case in three different reporters.
To introduce you to star paging.

CITATION RULES: Use *The Bluebook: A Uniform System of Citation*, 17th ed., Rules 10.2, 10.2.1, 10.2.2, 10.3, 10.4, 10.5 and Tables 1, 6 and 11. Use the format for court documents and legal memoranda and assume that the case citation appears in a citation sentence.

Locate 524 U.S. 321 to answer Questions 1-9.

1.   Find 524 U.S. 321. This is the official reporter version of the case. What is the case name? Use correct form (Rule 10.2).

2.   On what date was the case decided?

3.   What is the docket number of the case?

4.   Which party is the respondent?

5.   Which Justice wrote the opinion of the court?

6.   Which Justice wrote a dissenting opinion?

7.   What was the lower court cite of this case, on its way up to the Supreme Court? Note: You are looking for the cite of a F.3d case.

8.   How did the Supreme Court act on the judgment of the court below?

9.   Who argued the cause for the United States?

To answer Questions 10-17 you will need to compare the case from Question 1 in the two unofficial versions, S. Ct., L. Ed., of this opinion.

10.   Find the appropriate book of vol. 118 of the *Supreme Court Reporter* (S. Ct.), published by West, and vol. 141 of the *U.S. Supreme Court Reports—Lawyers' Edition* (L. Ed. 2d), published then by Lexis Publishing and now by LexisNexis. These two reporters are unofficial reporters for United States Supreme Court cases. Use the Cases Reported table at the front of S. Ct. and the Table of Cases Reported in the front of L. Ed. to find your case in both reporters.

        a. What is the S. Ct. cite?

        b. What is the L. Ed. cite?

11.   Examine the headnotes preceding the opinions. On what page of which reporter does the ninth West topic and key number appear? (Note: A small key-shaped symbol accompanies the West topic and key number.)

12.   State the West topic and key number from the preceding question.

13.   Each headnote corresponds to a particular part of the Court's opinion. Examine the opinion in S. Ct. and look for references to the headnote numbers (boldface numbers in brackets **[1]**). On what page of the S. Ct. **opinion** is there a reference to the ninth West headnote?

14.   Star paging enables attorneys using L. Ed. or S. Ct. to cite U.S. paging without using U.S. itself. Star paging in L. Ed. is shown thus: **[405 US 729]**. Star paging in S. Ct. is indicated thus: ⊥**729**   Looking at the *Supreme Court Reporter* and using star paging ⊥, state the page of *United States Reports* (U.S.) on which the corresponding material related to the ninth **[9]** West headnote begins.

15.   Notice that the two unofficial reporters have different headnotes. How many headnotes are in the *U.S. Supreme Court Reports, Lawyers' Edition*?

16.   Question 8 asked you about the **disposition** of the case, that is, how the Supreme Court treated the judgment of the court below. The **holding** is another part of a case, the application of rules of law to the specific key facts in the case. What is the holding of this case as to whether the defendant's forfeiture of the entire $357,144.00 at issue was constitutional? You may want to review the syllabus of the case.

17.   Which section of Title 31 of U.S.C. requires an individual who is leaving the United States with more than $10,000.00 in currency to report it?

ASSIGNMENT TWO
SUPREME COURT REPORTERS AND PARTS OF A CASE
EXERCISE D

GOALS OF THIS ASSIGNMENT:
To familiarize you with the parts of a case in three different reporters.
To introduce you to star paging.

CITATION RULES: Use *The Bluebook: A Uniform System of Citation*, 17th ed., Rules 10.2, 10.2.1, 10.2.2, 10.3, 10.4, 10.5 and Tables 1, 6 and 11. Use the format for court documents and legal memoranda and assume that the case citation appears in a citation sentence.

Locate 514 U.S. 52 to answer Questions 1-9.

1. Find 514 U.S. 52. This is the official reporter version of the case. What is the case name? Use correct form (Rule 10.2).

2. On what date was the case decided?

3. What is the docket number of the case?

4. Which party is the petitioner?

5. Which Justice wrote the opinion of the court?

6. Which Justice wrote a dissenting opinion?

7.   What was the lower court cite of this case, on its way up to the Supreme Court? Note: You are looking for the cite of a F.3d case.

8.   How did the Supreme Court act on the judgment of the court below?

9.   Who argued the cause for the petitioner?

To answer Questions 10-17, you will need to compare the case from Question 1 in the two unofficial versions, S. Ct., L. Ed., of this opinion.

10.   Find the appropriate book of vol. 115 of the *Supreme Court Reporter* (S. Ct.), published by West, and vol. 131 of the *U.S. Supreme Court Reports—Lawyers' Edition* (L. Ed. 2d), published then by Lexis Law Publishing and now by LexisNexis. These two reporters are unofficial reporters for United States Supreme Court cases. Use the Cases Reported table at the front of S. Ct. and the Table of Cases Reported in the front of L. Ed. to find your case in both reporters.

a. What is the S. Ct. cite?

b. What is the L. Ed. cite?

11.   Examine the headnotes preceding the opinions. On what page of which reporter does the fifth West topic and key number appear? (Note: A small key-shaped symbol accompanies the West topic and key number.)

12.   State the West topic and key number from the preceding question.

13.   Each headnote corresponds to a particular part of the Court's opinion. Examine the opinion in S. Ct. and look for references to the headnote numbers (boldface numbers in brackets **[1]**). On what page of the S. Ct. **opinion** is there a reference to the fifth West headnote?

14.   Star paging enables attorneys using L. Ed. or S. Ct. to cite U.S. paging without using U.S. itself. Star paging in L. Ed. is shown thus: **[405 US 729]**. Star paging in S. Ct. is indicated thus: ⊥**729**   Looking at the *Supreme Court Reporter* and using star paging ⊥, state the page of *United States Reports* (U.S.) on which the corresponding material related to the fifth **[5]** West headnote begins.

15.   Notice that the two unofficial reporters have different headnotes. How many headnotes are in the *U.S. Supreme Court Reports, Lawyers' Edition*?

16.   Question 8 asked you about the **disposition** of the case, that is, how the Supreme Court treated the judgment of the court below. The **holding** is another part of a case, the application of rules of law to the specific key facts in the case. What is the holding of this case as to whether the contract between securities brokerage firm and customers permitted an arbitration panel to award punitive damages to customers? You may want to review the syllabus of the case.

17.   In which title of the U.S.C. is the Federal Arbitration Act located?

ASSIGNMENT THREE
REGIONAL REPORTERS
EXERCISE A

GOALS OF THIS ASSIGNMENT:
To acquaint you with the Table of Cases in the digests.
To compare the features of regional reporters.

CITATION RULES: For this assignment when citing a case, assume you are citing the case in a legal document that will be submitted to a state court that does not require parallel cites.

Assume you want to find the unofficial (regional) text of *State v. Gilmore*, a 1986 Supreme Court of New Jersey case. When you know the case name and jurisdiction, but do not know the citation, one way to find the citation is to look it up in a digest table of cases. Look up *State v. Gilmore* in the Table of Cases volume in either the *New Jersey Digest 2d*, the *Atlantic Digest 2d*, or the *Tenth Decennial Digest, Part 1*.

1.   What is the full citation of the case? (Remember, this means name, cite, jurisdiction, court and year according to Rule 10 of *The Bluebook*.)

Find the unofficial report of the case in the *Atlantic Reporter* and answer Questions 2-8.

2.   Notice the long, one-paragraph summary of the facts and holding. This is called the synopsis and West editors wrote it. According to the synopsis, did the Supreme Court affirm or reverse the Superior Court, Appellate Division decision?

3.   Notice the headnotes (one-sentence summaries of points of law). All headnotes in the regional reporters that follow West topic and key numbers are written by West editors. How many headnotes are listed here?

4.   A topic and key number precede each headnote in a regional reporter, like those you saw in Assignment Two. What is the topic and key number for the second headnote?

Never quote from or cite to the synopsis or headnotes. You can, however, search them on WESTLAW, along with the topics and key numbers. Cases are divided into different parts, called **fields** on WESTLAW and **segments** on LEXIS. Fields and segments can be searched separately, or with the rest of the case.

5. Remember, you can find the part of the opinion that corresponds to the second headnote by looking for the corresponding boldface number in brackets in the opinion. On what page of the opinion do you find the corresponding text?

6. Read the opinion. Under what article of the New Jersey Constitution did the court first analyze the defendant's constitutional right to a trial by an impartial jury?

7. Look at the beginning of the case. What is the official cite, which is given just above the name of the case?

8. Look at the title page of the *Atlantic Reporter* volume. List **five** states covered in the *Atlantic Reporter.*

9. Using your textbook or *The Bluebook: A Uniform System of Citation*, state the regional reporters in which the following states' reports are found:

        a. Nebraska

        b. Ohio

        c. Rhode Island

In this assignment, you used the table of cases in a digest to find the cite to a case. You then found that case in a regional reporter. Does your own state have an official reporter? Ask your instructor.

ASSIGNMENT THREE
REGIONAL REPORTERS
EXERCISE B

GOALS OF THIS ASSIGNMENT:
To acquaint you with the Table of Cases in the digests.
To compare the features of regional reporters.

CITATION RULES: For this assignment when citing a case, assume you are citing the case in a legal document that will be submitted to a state court that does not require parallel cites.

Assume you want to find the unofficial (regional) text of *Adamson v. Hill*, a 1969 Supreme Court of Kansas case. When you know the case name and jurisdiction, but do not know the citation, one way to find the citation is to look it up in a digest table of cases. Look up *Adamson v. Hill* in the Table of Cases volume in either the *Kansas Digest 2d, the Pacific Digest* (Beginning 367 P.2d) or the *Eighth Decennial Digest*.

1.   What is the full citation of the case? (Remember, this means name, cite, jurisdiction, court and year according to Rule 10 of *The Bluebook*.)

Find the unofficial report of the case in the *Pacific Reporter* and answer Questions 2-8.

2.   Notice the long, one-paragraph summary of the facts and holding. This is called the synopsis and West editors wrote it. According to the synopsis, did the Supreme Court affirm or reverse and remand with directions the decision of the Crawford District Court?

3.   Notice the headnotes (one-sentence summaries of points of law). All headnotes in the regional reporters that follow West topic and key numbers are written by West editors. How many headnotes are listed here?

4.   A topic and key number precede each headnote in a regional reporter, like those you saw in Assignment Two. What is the topic and key number for the sixth headnote?

Never quote from or cite to the synopsis or headnotes. You can, however, search them on WESTLAW, along with the topics and key numbers. Cases are divided into different parts, called fields on WESTLAW and segments on LEXIS. Fields and segments can be searched separately, or with the rest of the case.

5.   Remember, you can find the part of the opinion that corresponds to the sixth headnote by looking for the corresponding boldface number in brackets in the opinion. On what page of the opinion do you find the corresponding text?

6.   Read the opinion. Did the court hold that the wife was not entitled to the benefit of the adjudication of the defendant's negligence and proximate cause in her husband's case?

7.   Look at the beginning of the case. What is the official cite, which is given just above the name of the case?

8.   Look at the title page of the *Pacific Reporter* volume. List **five** states covered in the *Pacific Reporter*.

9.   Using your textbook or *The Bluebook: A Uniform System of Citation*, state the regional reporters in which the following states' reports are found:

              a. Alabama

              b. Colorado

              c. Massachusetts

In this assignment, you used the table of cases in a digest to find the cite to a case. You then found that case in a regional reporter. Does your own state have an official reporter? Ask your instructor.

ASSIGNMENT THREE
REGIONAL REPORTERS
EXERCISE C

GOALS OF THIS ASSIGNMENT:
To acquaint you with the Table of Cases in the digests.
To compare the features of regional reporters.

CITATION RULES: For this assignment when citing a case, assume you are citing the case in a legal document that will be submitted to a state court that does not require parallel cites.

Assume you want to find the unofficial (regional) text of *Auric v. Continental Casualty Company*, a 1983 Wisconsin Supreme Court case. When you know the case name and jurisdiction, but do not know the citation, one way to find the citation is to look it up in a digest table of cases. Look up *Auric v. Continental Casualty Company* in the Table of Cases volume in either the *Wisconsin Digest, the North Western Digest 2d* or the *Ninth Decennial Digest, Part 2.*

1.   What is the full citation of the case? (Remember, this means name, cite, jurisdiction, court and year according to Rule 10 of *The Bluebook*.)

Find the unofficial report of the case in the *North Western Reporter* and answer Questions 2-8.

2.   Notice the long, one-paragraph summary of the facts and holding. This is called the synopsis and West editors wrote it. According to the synopsis, did the Supreme Court affirm or reverse with directions the decision of the Circuit Court?

3.   Notice the headnotes (one-sentence summaries of points of law). All headnotes in the regional reporters that follow West topic and key numbers are written by West editors. How many headnotes are listed here?

4.   A topic and key number precede each headnote in a regional reporter, like those you saw in Assignment Two. What is the topic and key number for the first headnote?

Never quote from or cite to the synopsis or headnotes. You can, however, search them on WESTLAW, along with the topics and key numbers. Cases are divided into different parts, called **fields** on WESTLAW and **segments** on LEXIS. Fields and segments can be searched separately, or with the rest of the case.

5.   Remember, you can find the part of the opinion that corresponds to the first headnote by looking for the corresponding boldface number in brackets in the opinion. On what page of the opinion do you find the corresponding text?

6.   Read the opinion. Did the court hold that the beneficiary of a will may maintain an action against an attorney who negligently drafted or supervised the execution of the will even though the beneficiary is not in privity with the attorney?

7.   Look at the beginning of the case. What is the official cite, which is given just above the name of the case?

8.   Look at the title page of a *North Western Reporter* volume. List the **seven** states covered in the *North Western Reporter*.

9.   Using your textbook or *The Bluebook: A Uniform System of Citation*, state the regional reporters in which the following states' reports are found:

        a. Arkansas

        b. Mississippi

        c. Wyoming

In this assignment, you used the table of cases in a digest to find the cite to a case. You then found that case in a regional reporter. Does your own state have an official reporter? Ask your instructor.

ASSIGNMENT THREE
REGIONAL REPORTERS
EXERCISE D

GOALS OF THIS ASSIGNMENT:
To acquaint you with the Table of Cases in the digests.
To compare the features of the regional reporters.

CITATION RULES: For this assignment when citing a case, assume you are citing the case in a legal document that will be submitted to a state court that does not require parallel cites.

Assume you want to find the unofficial (regional) text of *Stewart v. Williams*, a 1979 Supreme Court of Georgia case. When you know the case name and jurisdiction, but do not know the citation, one way to find the citation is to look it up in a digest table of cases. Look up *Stewart v. Williams* in the Table of Cases volume in either the *Georgia Digest 2d, the South Eastern Digest 2d* or the *Ninth Decennial Digest, Part 1*.

1. What is the full citation of the case? (Remember, this means name, cite, jurisdiction, court and year according to Rule 10 of *The Bluebook*.)

Find the unofficial report of the case in the *South Eastern Reporter* and answer Questions 2-8.

2. Notice the long, one-paragraph summary of the facts and holding. This is called the synopsis and West editors wrote it. According to the synopsis, did the Supreme Court affirm or reverse the decision of the Court of Appeals?

3. Notice the headnotes (one-sentence summaries of points of law). All headnotes in the regional reporters that follow West topic and key numbers are written by West editors. How many headnotes are listed here?

4. A topic and key number precede each headnote in a regional reporter, like those you saw in Assignment Two. What is the topic and key number for the third headnote?

Never quote from or cite to the synopsis or headnotes. You can, however, search them on WESTLAW, along with the topics and key numbers. Cases are divided into different parts, called **fields** on WESTLAW and **segments** on LEXIS. Fields and segments can be searched separately, or with the rest of the case.

5. Remember, you can find the part of the opinion that corresponds to the third headnote by looking for the corresponding boldface number in brackets in the opinion. On what page of the opinion do you find the corresponding text??

6. Read the opinion. Did the court hold that the burden of proving a reasonable execution of a warrant was on the defendant?

7. Look at the beginning of the case. This case proceeded on appeal?

8. Look at the title page of the *South Eastern Reporter* volume. List the **five** states covered in the *South Eastern Reporter*.

9. Using you textbook or *The Bluebook: A Uniform System of Citation*, state the regional reporters in which the following states' reports are found:

　　　　a. Connecticut

　　　　b. Hawaii

　　　　c. Minnesota

In this assignment, you used the table of cases in a digest to find the cite to a case. You then found that case in a regional reporter. Does your own state have an official reporter? Ask your instructor.

ASSIGNMENT FOUR
FINDING CASES–DIGESTS
EXERCISE A

GOALS OF THIS ASSIGNMENT:
To introduce you to West digests.
To give you practice at the various methods of using digests.

CITATION RULES: For this assignment when citing a case, assume you are citing the case in a legal document that will be submitted to a state court that does not require parallel cites.

Let's start our digest research by using what some have called the "one good case" approach. The issue in our research problem deals with a criminal defendant's right to a trial by an impartial jury without discrimination on the basis of religious principles, race, color, ancestry, national origin or sex. The relevant case we will use is the one you worked with in **Assignment Three**, *State v. Gilmore*, a 1986 Supreme Court of New Jersey case. If the citation is unavailable, check the Table of Cases in the digest.

1. To review, what is the regional cite for the case?

2. What West topic and key number covers our issue? Look up the case in the regional reporter if you don't remember the answer to this question.

3. We now have a West topic and key number to begin our digest research. First, let's find out just what this topic and key number represent. Go to either 1) the *New Jersey Digest 2d*; 2) the *Atlantic Digest 2d*; or 3) the *Tenth Decennial Digest, Part 1* (in that order of preference). Find the analysis outline at the very beginning of the topic from Question 2 in your digest. Examine the list of key numbers. What does the key number from Question 2 stand for? Include all relevant topics of which your key number may be a subtopic.

You will be using the same digest to answer Questions 4-10.

4. Go to your key number and look at the cases listed under it. Is there a New Jersey Supreme Court case from 1987 digested under this topic and key number? If so, provide the name of the case and the regional citation.

5.   Now you will use the topic approach. The topic approach merely involves reading the list of key numbers at the beginning of the topic (the topic outline) and looking for relevant key numbers. Go back to the topic outline (called "Analysis") for **Jury**. If you were looking for cases discussing the offenses in general for which a person has a right to a jury trial in a criminal prosecution for a misdemeanor, under what topic and key number would you look?

6.   Look up that key number. State the name of the 1991 New Jersey Superior Court Appellate Division case listed.

7.   Now you will use the subject approach. Look in the Descriptive Word Index volumes (either at the beginning or the end of the set). Using the descriptive word approach, find the topic and key number cases dealing with whether or not a juror's opinions about the death penalty are grounds for challenges for cause or disqualification. To what topic and key number are you referred?

8.   Look up the topic and key number and find a 1989 New Jersey Supreme Court case. List the full citation of the case in correct form.

How to update your research using a federal, state or regional digest:

1).   **Current digest volumes are supplemented by pocket parts.**

2).   **If there are no pocket parts, look instead for a free standing pamphlet that updates that particular volume.**

3).   **Check the "Closing with Cases Reported in" section on the second page of the pocket part or pamphlet.**

4).   **Go the case reporter that you identified in step 3. Look in the digest sections in the back of all bound volumes and in the front of all advance sheets beginning with the volume listed in the "Closing with Cases Reporter in"to see if any recent cases have appeared under your topic and key number.**

Now, examine the pocket part of the digest volume you used to answer the last question.

If you were using the Decennial Digest, there are no pocket parts; normally you would have to examine all volumes of the General Digest, but for this exercise, check only the last volume.

9.   Look at the "Closing with Cases Reported in" statement on the second page of the pocket part. What is the last volume of A.2d that the digest pocket part covers?

10.   Are there any pamphlet supplements to the digest? If so, check them for the topic and key number from Question 7. Find the last digest pamphlet for A.2d. What is the last volume of A.2d covered in the pamphlet?

Now go the *Atlantic Reporter 2d*.

11.   Normally, you would start with the first volume not covered by the digest pamphlet supplement. Each bound reporter volume has a small digest section in the back. You would check the digest sections of all of the bound reporters. For this assignment, however, check **only** the **most recent** bound volume. If any cases are digested under your topic and key number, list the full citation here.

12. Now check the *Atlantic Reporter's* advance sheets. Bound volumes are updated by paperbound advance sheets. Several advance sheets are bound together into a reporter. In advance sheets, the digest section is in the front, just before the decisions begin. Normally, you would look in all of the advance sheets. For this assignment, however, check **only** the **most recent** advance sheet. If any cases are digested under your topic and key number, list the full citation here.

One great advantage of the West topic and key number system is that you can use it for **all jurisdictions**. The same topic and key number will work in Kansas, Arkansas, Georgia, all states, and all federal courts. Different West digests will group jurisdictions in different ways. For example, the *Kansas Digest* contains Kansas cases and federal cases arising in Kansas. Each West state digest has similar coverage.

Regional digests contain state cases from each state covered by that particular region. The federal digests cover all of the federal courts, and the Decennial and General Digests, all of the state and federal jurisdictions. Use the most appropriate digest in your library, and provide the full citation, in correct form, for the following cases. Search under the topic and key number from **Question 2**.

13. Check the *Virginia and West Virginia Digest*, the *South Eastern Digest 2d*, or the *Tenth Decennial Digest, Part 1*. Provide the full citation, in correct form, of the 1987 West Virginia Supreme Court of Appeals case digested under the topic and key number from Question 2.

14. Check the *Federal Practice Digest 4th*. Is there a 1990 Ninth circuit court of appeals cases arising from California digested under this topic and key number? If so, provide full citations in correct form.

GOALS OF THIS ASSIGNMENT:
To introduce you to West digests.
To give you practice at the various methods of using digests

CITATION RULES: For this assignment when citing a case, assume you are citing the case in a legal document that will be submitted to a state court that does not require parallel cites.

Let's start our digest research by using what some have called the "one good case" approach. The issue in our research problem concerns the four concurrent conditions needed to establish res judicata. The relevant case we will use is the one you worked with in **Assignment Three**, *Adamson v. Hill*, a 1969 Kansas Supreme Court case. If the citation is unavailable, check the digest's Table of Cases.

1. To review, what is the regional cite for the case?

2. What West topic and key number covers our issue? Look up the case in the regional reporter if you don't remember the answer to this question.

3. We now have a West topic and key number to begin our digest research. First, let's find out just what this topic and key number represent. Go to either 1) the *Kansas Digest 2d*; 2) the *Pacific Digest* (Beginning 367 P.2d); or 3) the *Eighth Decennial Digest* (in that order of preference). Find the analysis outline at the very beginning of the topic from Question 2 in your digest. Examine the list of key numbers. What does the key number from Question 2 stand for? Include all relevant topics of which your key number may be a subtopic.

    You will be using the same digest to answer Questions 4-10.

4. Go to your key number and look at the cases listed under it. Is there a Supreme Court of Kansas case from 1971 digested under this topic and key number? If so, provide the name of the case and the regional citation.

5.   Now you will use the topic approach. The topic approach merely involves reading the list of key numbers at the beginning of the topic (the topic outline) and looking for relevant key numbers. Go back to the topic outline (called "Analysis") for **Judgment**. If you were looking for cases concerning parties of record and privies in general who may take advantage of the bar of causes of action and defenses, under what topic and key number would you look?

6.   Look up that key number. State the name of the 1970 Supreme Court of Kansas case as listed.

7.   Now you will use the subject approach. Look in the Descriptive Word Index volumes (either at the beginning or the end of the set). Using the descriptive word approach, find the topic and key number for cases dealing with a nunc pro tunc order amending or correcting a previous judgment, such as when an interest is eliminated from a subsequent written draft of an oral judgment. To what topic and key number are you referred?

8.   Look up the topic and key number and find a 1975 Supreme Court of Kansas case. List the full citation of the case in correct form.

How to update your research using a federal, state or regional digest:

1). **Current digest volumes are supplemented by pocket parts.**

2). **If there are no pocket parts, look instead for a free standing pamphlet that updates that particular volume.**

3). **Check the "Closing with Cases Reported in" section on the second page of the pocket part or pamphlet.**

4). **Go the case reporter that you identified in step 3. Look in the digest sections in the back of all bound volumes and in the front of all advance sheets beginning with the volume listed in the "Closing with Cases Reporter in" to see if any recent cases have appeared under your topic and key number.**

Now, examine the pocket part of the digest volume you used to answer the last question.
If you were using the Decennial Digest, there are no pocket parts; normally you would have to examine all volumes of the General Digest, but for this exercise, check only the last volume.

9.   Look at the "Closing with Cases Reported in" statement on the second page of the pocket part. What is the last volume of P.3d that the digest pocket part covers?

10. Are there any pamphlet supplements to the digest? If so, check them for the topic and key number from Question 7. Find the last digest pamphlet for P.3d. What is the last volume of P.3d covered in the pamphlet?

Now go the *Pacific Reporter 3d.*

11. Normally, you would start with the first volume not covered by the digest pamphlet supplement. Each bound reporter volume has a small digest section in the back. You would check the digest sections of all of the bound reporters. For this assignment, however, check **only** the **most recent** bound volume. If any cases are digested under your topic and key number, list the full citation here.

12.   Now check the *Pacific Reporter's* advance sheets. Bound volumes are updated by paperbound advance sheets. Several advance sheets are bound together into a reporter. In advance sheets, the digest section is in the front, just before the decisions begin. Normally, you would look in all of the advance sheets. For this assignment, however, check **only** the **most recent** advance sheet. If any cases are digested under your topic and key number, list the full citation here.

One great advantage of the West topic and key number system is that you can use it for **all jurisdictions**. The same topic and key number will work in Kansas, Arkansas, Georgia, all states, and all federal courts. Different West digests will group jurisdictions in different ways. For example, the *Kansas Digest* contains Kansas cases and federal cases arising in Kansas. Each West state digest has similar coverage.

Regional digests contain state cases from each state covered by that particular region. The federal digests cover all of the federal courts, and the Decennial and General Digests, all of the state and federal jurisdictions. Use the most appropriate digest in your library, and provide the full citation, in correct form, for the following cases. Search under the topic and key number from **Question 2**.

13.   Check the *Rhode Island Digest*, the *Atlantic Digest 2d*, or the *Eighth Decennial Digest*. Provide the full citation, in correct form, of the 1972 Rhode Island Supreme Court case digested under the topic and key number from Question 2.

14.   Check the *Federal Practice Digest 4ᵗʰ*. Is there a 1989 Fourth Circuit Court of Appeals cases arising from Maryland digested under this topic and key number? If so, provide the full citation in correct form.

ASSIGNMENT FOUR
FINDING CASES–DIGESTS
EXERCISE C

GOALS OF THIS ASSIGNMENT:
To introduce you to West digests.
To give you practice at the various methods of using digests.

CITATION RULES: For this assignment when citing a case, assume you are citing the case in a legal document that will be submitted to a state court that does not require parallel cites.

Let's start our digest research by using what some have called the "one good case" approach. The issue in our research problem is whether an attorney is liable to third parties for acts committed in the exercise of his duties as an attorney. The relevant case we will use is the one you worked with in **Assignment Three**, *Auric v. Continental Casualty Company*, a 1983 Wisconsin Supreme Court case. If the citation is unavailable, check the Table of Cases in the digest.

1.   To review, what is the regional cite for the case?

2.   What West topic and key number covers our issue? Look up the case in the regional reporter if you don't remember the answer to this question.

3.   We now have a West topic and key number to begin our digest research. First, let's find out just what this topic and key number represent. Go to either 1) the *Wisconsin Digest*; 2) the *North Western Digest 2d*; or 3) the *Ninth Decennial Digest, Part 2* (in that order of preference). Find the analysis outline at the very beginning of the topic from Question 2 in your digest. Examine the list of key numbers. What does the key number from Question 2 stand for? Include all relevant topics of which your key number may be a subtopic.

You will be using the same digest to answer Questions 4-10.

4.   Go to your key number and look at the cases listed under it. Is there **another** Wisconsin Supreme Court case from 1983 (besides *Auric*) digested under this topic and key number? If so, provide the name of the case and the regional citation.

5. Now you will use the topic approach. The topic approach merely involves reading the list of key numbers at the beginning of the topic (the topic outline) and looking for relevant key numbers. Go back to the topic outline (called "Analysis") for **Attorney and Client**. If you were looking for cases that discuss the duties and liabilities of an attorney to a client for negligent acts and omissions of the attorney in general, under what topic and key number would you look?

6. Look up that key number. State the name of the 1985 Wisconsin Supreme Court case listed.

7. Now you will use the subject approach. Look in the Descriptive Word Index volumes (either at the beginning or the end of the set). Using the descriptive word approach, find the topic and key number for cases concerning whether or not in disciplinary proceedings, alcoholism is a defense or excuse to charges of unprofessional attorney conduct brought by a client. To what topic and key number are you referred?

8. Look up the topic and key number and find the 1985 Wisconsin Supreme Court cases **specifically mentioning alcoholism**. List the full citation of the **first listed** case appearing in volume 365 in correct form.

How to update your research using a federal, state or regional digest:

1). Current digest volumes are supplemented by pocket parts.

2). If there are no pocket parts, look instead for a free standing pamphlet that updates that particular volume.

3). Check the "Closing with Cases Reported in" section on the second page of the pocket part or pamphlet.

4). Go the case reporter that you identified in step 3. Look in the digest sections in the back of all bound volumes and in the front of all advance sheets beginning with the volume listed in the "Closing with Cases Reporter in" to see if any recent cases have appeared under your topic and key number.

Now, examine the pocket part of the digest volume you used to answer the last question.
If you were using the Decennial Digest, there are no pocket parts; normally you would have to examine all volumes of the General Digest, but for this exercise, check only the last volume.

9. Look at the "Closing with Cases Reported in" statement on the second page of the pocket part. What is the last volume of N.W.2d that the digest pocket part covers?

10. Are there any pamphlet supplements to the digest? If so, check them for the topic and key number from Question 7. Find the last digest pamphlet for N.W.2d. What is the last volume of N.W.2d covered in the pamphlet?

Now go the *North Western Reporter 2d.*

11. Normally, you would start with the first volume not covered by the digest pamphlet supplement. Each bound reporter volume has a small digest section in the back. You would check the digest sections of all of the bound reporters. For this assignment, however, check **only** the **most recent** bound volume. If any cases are digested under your topic and key number, list the full citation here.

12.   Now check the *North Western Reporter's* advance sheets. Bound volumes are updated by paperbound advance sheets. Several advance sheets are bound together into a reporter. In advance sheets, the digest section is in the front, just before the decisions begin. Normally, you would look in all of the advance sheets. For this assignment, however, check **only** the **most recent** advance sheet. If any cases are digested under your topic and key number, list the full citation here.

One great advantage of the West topic and key number system is that you can use it for **all jurisdictions**. The same topic and key number will work in Kansas, Arkansas, Georgia, all states, and all federal courts. Different West digests will group jurisdictions in different ways. For example, the *Kansas Digest* contains Kansas cases and federal cases arising in Kansas. Each West state digest has similar coverage.

Regional digests contain state cases from each state covered by that particular region. The federal digests cover all of the federal courts, and the Decennial and General Digests, all of the state and federal jurisdictions. Use the most appropriate digest in your library, and provide the full citation, in correct form, for the following cases. Search under the topic and key number from **Question 2**.

13.   Check the *Colorado Digest 2d*, the *Pacific Digest* (Beginning 585 P.2d), or the *Ninth Decennial Digest, Part 2*. Provide the full citation, in correct form, of the 1985 Colorado Court of Appeals case digested under the topic and key number from Question 2.

14.   Check the *Federal Practice Digest 4ᵗʰ*. Is there a 1990 Seventh Circuit Court of Appeals case arising from Illinois digested under this topic and key number? If so, provide the full citation in correct form.

ASSIGNMENT FOUR
FINDING CASES–DIGEST
EXERCISE D

GOALS OF THIS ASSIGNMENT:
To introduce you to West digest.
To give you practice at the various methods of using digests.

CITATION RULES: For this assignment when citing a case, assume you are citing the case in a legal document that will be submitted to a state court that does not require parallel cites.

Let's start our digest research by using what some have called the "one good case" approach. The issue in our research problem is whether in a false imprisonment action, a plaintiff has made a prima facie case of false imprisonment by showing an intentional deprivation of his liberty. The relevant case we will use is the one you worked with in **Assignment Three**, *Stewart v. Williams*, a 1979 Georgia Supreme Court case. If the citation is unavailable, check the Table of Cases in the digest.

1.   To review, what is the regional cite for the case?

2.   What West topic and key number covers our issue? Look up the case in the regional reporter if you don't remember the answer to this question.

3.   We now have a West topic and key number to begin our digest research. First, let's find out just what this topic and key number represent. Go to either 1) the *Georgia Digest 2d*; 2) the *South Eastern Digest 2d*; or 3) the *Ninth Decennial Digest, Part 1* (in that order of preference). Find the analysis outline at the very beginning of the topic from Question 2 in your digest. Examine the list of key numbers. What does the key number from Question 2 stand for? Include all relevant topics of which your key number may be a subtopic.

You will be using the same digest to answer Questions 4-10.

4.   Go to your key number and look at the cases listed under it. Is there a Georgia Court of Appeals Court case from 1979 digested under this topic and key number? If so, provide the name of the **first listed** case appearing in volume 259 and the regional citation.

5. Now you will use the topic approach. The topic approach merely involves reading the list of key numbers at the beginning of the topic (the topic outline) and looking for relevant key numbers. Go back to the topic outline (called "Analysis") for **False Imprisonment**. If you were looking for cases concerning civil actions for false imprisonment and the time to sue and limitations, under what topic and key number would you look?

6. Look up that key number. State the name of the 1979 Georgia Court of Appeals case listed.

7. Now you will use the subject approach. Look in the Descriptive Word Index volumes (either at the beginning or the end of the set). Using the descriptive word approach, find the topic and key number for cases dealing whether or not damages for mental suffering can be awarded in false imprisonment actions. To what topic and key number are you referred?

8. Look up the topic and key number and find a 1979 Georgia Court of Appeals case. List the full citation of the case in correct form.

How to update your research using a federal, state or regional digest:

1).   **Current digest volumes are supplemented by pocket parts.**

2).   **If there are no pocket parts, look instead for a free standing pamphlet that updates that particular volume.**

3).   **Check the "Closing with Cases Reported in" section on the second page of the pocket part or pamphlet.**

4).   **Go the case reporter that you identified in step 3. Look in the digest sections in the back of all bound volumes and in the front of all advance sheets beginning with volume listed in the "Closing with Cases Reporter in" to see if any recent cases have appeared under your topic and key number.**

Now, examine the pocket part of the digest volume you used to answer the last question.
If you were using the Decennial Digest, there are no pocket parts; normally you would have to examine all volumes of the General Digest, but for this exercise, check only the last volume.

9.   Look at the "Closing with Cases Reported in" statement on the second page of the pocket part. What is the last volume of S.E.2d that the digest pocket part covers?

10.   Are there any pamphlet supplements to the digest? If so, check them for the topic and key number from Question 7. Find the last digest pamphlet for S.E.2d. What is the last volume of S.E.2d covered in the pamphlet?

Now go the *South Eastern Reporter.*

11.   Normally, you would start with the first volume not covered by the digest pamphlet supplement. Each bound reporter volume has a small digest section in the back. You would check the digest sections of all of the bound reporters. For this assignment, however, check **only** the **most recent** bound volume. If any cases are digested under your topic and key number, list the full citation here.

12.   Now check the *South Eastern Reporter's* advance sheets. Bound volumes are updated by paperbound advance sheets. Several advance sheets are bound together into a reporter. In advance sheets, the digest section is in the front, just before the decisions begin. Normally, you would look in all of the advance sheets. For this assignment, however, check **only** the **most recent** advance sheet. If any cases are digested under your topic and key number, list the full citation here.

One great advantage of the West topic and key number system is that you can use it for **all jurisdictions**. The same topic and key number will work in Kansas, Arkansas, Georgia, all states, and all federal courts. Different West digests will group jurisdictions in different ways. For example, the *Kansas Digest* contains Kansas cases and federal cases arising in Kansas. Each West state digest has similar coverage.

Regional digests contain state cases from each state covered by that particular region. The federal digests cover all of the federal courts, and the Decennial and General Digests, all of the state and federal jurisdictions. Use the most appropriate digest in your library, and provide the full citation, in correct form, for the following cases. Search under the topic and key number from **Question 2**.

13.   Check the *Wisconsin Digest*, the *North Western Digest 2d*, or the *Ninth Decennial Digest, Part 1*. Provide the full citation, in correct form, of the 1981 Wisconsin Supreme Court case digested under the topic and key number from Question 2. Note: You will need to look up the case to cite the name properly.

14.   Check the *Federal Practice Digest 4th*. Is there a 1997 federal district court case arising from Kansas digested under this topic and key number? If so, provide the full citation in correct form omitting subsequent history.

ASSIGNMENT FIVE
UPDATING CASES–SHEPARD'S CITATORS
EXERCISE A

GOAL OF THIS ASSIGNMENT:
To teach you how to identify a parallel cite, case history, and case treatment in a Shepard's entry either in paper or online.
To show you the usefulness of the *National Reporter Blue Book*.

SECTION I: Complete Questions 1a-14a in Section I if your library has the Shepard's volumes available in print.

CITATION RULES: When a case cite appears in your answers, use the standard abbreviation for the reporter as found in *The Bluebook: A Uniform System of Citation*, 17th ed. It may differ substantially from the Shepard's abbreviation.

Questions 1a-4a require you to Shepardize the same case you worked with in Assignments Three and Four: *State v. Gilmore*, 511 A.2d 1150 (N.J. 1986). Find the case in the <u>bound</u> *Shepard's Atlantic Citations* volumes that contain cites to it.

1a.   Shepardize the case. What is its parallel cite?

2a.   Has an Arizona case cited the *Gilmore* case? If so, state its cite as listed in Shepard's. Remember, Shepard's in print does not list the first page of the case, but only the actual page that cites your case.

3a.   What is the cite of the decision that distinguished the *Gilmore* case?

4a.   Has an A.L.R.3d annotation cited *Gilmore*? If so, state the cite.

Reshelve Shepard's Citations.

5a.   Look up the case in your answer to Question 2. Does this case concern a criminal defendant's right to a trial by an impartial jury without discrimination on the basis of race?

Now, you will Shepardize a U.S. Supreme Court case, *Block v. Neal*, 460 U.S. 289, 103 S. Ct. 1089, 75 L. Ed. 2d 67. Examine the spine of *Shepard's United States Citations–Case Edition*, Volumes 1.1 - 1.10 and find the volume in which your case appears to answer Questions 6a - 14a.

6a.   How does Shepard's show parallel cites?

7a.   What is the cite of the same case in federal district court?

8a.   What is the cite of the court of appeals case from the Fifth Circuit that explained the *Block* case?

9a.   What is the cite of the Iowa decision that cited the *Block* case?

10a.   What Fourth Circuit court of appeals case's dissent cited *Block*?

11a.   State the Shepard's entry for the A.L.R.2d annotation that cited *Block*.

12a.   Did the A.L.R. reference in the previous question appear in the annotation or its supplement? If you need help with this question, refer to the prefatory material entitled *Illustrative Citations*.

13a.   If your *Shepard's United States Citations–Case Edition* includes volumes covering L. Ed. cites, find the listing for the case from Question 6 under its L. Ed. 2d cite. What is the cite of the court of appeals case from the Fourth Circuit that cited *Block* for the issue of law covered by the third headnote?

14a.   If your set includes volumes covering S. Ct. cites, find the listings for the case from Question 6 under its S. Ct. cite. What district court opinion from the Fifth Circuit cited a point of law from West headnote number 3 of your case?

SECTION II: Complete the Questions 1b-14b in section II, if your library does NOT have the Shepard's volumes in print. Use Shepard's online.

CITATION RULES: When a case cite appears in your answers, use the standard abbreviation for the reporter as found in *The Bluebook: A Uniform System of Citation*, 17th ed., give the first page of the citing case, and give the pinpoint cite to the page on which the case you are Shepardizing is cited.

Questions 1b-5b require you to Shepardize the same case you worked with in Assignments Three and Four: *State v. Gilmore*, 511 A.2d 1150 (N.J. 1986). Logon to http://www.lexisnexis.com/shepards/ or http://www.lexisnexis.com/lawschool/

1b. Shepardize the case. What is its parallel cite to the official reporter?

2b. Has a 1988 Arizona case cited the *Gilmore* case? If so, state its regional cite.

3b. Click on the link to the case in your answer to Question 2. Does this case concern a criminal defendant's right to a trial by an impartial jury without discrimination on the basis of race?

4b. What is the regional cite of the 1988 New Jersey Superior Court decision that distinguished the *Gilmore* case?

5b. Has a 79 A.L.R.3d annotation cited *Gilmore*? If so, state the cite.

Now, you will Shepardize the case *Block v. Neal*, 460 U.S. 289. Custom Restrictions in Shepard's online allows you to limit your citing references by analysis, jurisdiction, headnote and date. Use Custom Restrictions to help you find the following cases:

6b. What are the parallel cites to *West's Supreme Court Reporter* and *U.S. Supreme Court Reports, Lawyers' Edition*?

7b. In the prior history, what is the cite of the same case in federal district court?

8b.   What is the cite of the 1988 court of appeals case from the Fifth Circuit that explained the *Block* case?

9b.   What is the cite of the 1983 Iowa decision that cited the *Block* case?

10b.   What 1987 Fourth Circuit court of appeals case's dissent cited *Block*?

11b.   State the Shepard's entry for the 23 A.L.R.2d annotation that cited *Block*.

12b.   Did the A.L.R. reference in the previous question appear in the annotation or its supplement?

13b.   What is the cite of the 1986 court of appeals case from the Fourth Circuit that cited *Block* for the issue of law covered by the third headnote in the L. Ed. 2d version of the *Block* case?

14b.   What 1990 federal district court opinion from the Fifth Circuit cited a point of law from *West's Supreme Court Reporter* headnote number 3 of your case?

Reshelve or Logoff Shepard's and find the *National Reporter Blue Book*.

15.   You can also locate the regional cite to a case if you have the official cite by using the *National Reporter Blue Book*. Use the *National Reporter Blue Book* and state the unofficial parallel cites for the official cites listed below. Abbreviate the names of the unofficial reporters according to *The Bluebook: A Uniform System of Citation*. Note: The set contains many volumes, organized in rough chronological order. Be certain that you use the volume that includes the official cite to your case. The date given with each cite will help you find it.

        a. 249 Neb. 376 (1996)

        b. 158 Miss. 505 (1930)

ASSIGNMENT FIVE
UPDATING CASES–SHEPARD'S CITATORS
EXERCISE B

GOAL OF THIS ASSIGNMENT:
To teach you how to identify a parallel cite, case history, and case treatment in a Shepard's entry either in paper or online.
To show you the usefulness of the *National Reporter Blue Book*.

SECTION I: Complete Questions 1a-14a in Section I if your library has the Shepard's volumes available in print.

CITATION RULES: When a case cite appears in your answers, use the standard abbreviation for the reporter as found in *The Bluebook: A Uniform System of Citation*, 17th ed. It may differ substantially from the Shepard's abbreviation.

Questions 1a-4a require you to Shepardize the same case you worked with in Assignments Three and Four: *Adamson v. Hill*, 449 P.2d 536 (Kan. 1969). Find the case in the <u>bound</u> *Shepard's Pacific Citations* volumes that contain cites to it.

1a.   Shepardize the case. What is its parallel cite?

2a.   Has a Colorado case cited the *Adamson* case? If so, state its cite as listed in Shepard's. Remember, Shepard's in print does not list the first page of the case, but only the actual page that cites your case.

3a.   What is the cite of the decision that distinguished the *Adamson* case?

4a.   Has an A.L.R.3d annotation cited *Adamson*? If so, state the cites.

Reshelve Shepard's Citations.

5a.   Look up the case in your answer to Question 2. Does this case concern asserting res judicata as collateral estoppel?

Now, you will Shepardize a U.S. Supreme Court case *United States v. Borden Co.*, 308 U.S. 188, 60 S. Ct. 182, 84 L. Ed. 181. Examine the spine of *Shepard's United States Citations–Case Edition*, Volumes 1.1 - 1.10 and find the volume in which your case appears to answer Questions 6a - 14a.

6a.   How does Shepard's show parallel cites?

7a.   What is the cite of the same case in federal district court?

8a.   What is the cite of the court of appeals case from the Ninth Circuit that explained the *Borden* case?

9a.   What is the cite of the Missouri decision that cited the *Borden* case?

10a.   What Fourth Circuit court of appeals case's dissent cited *Borden*?

11a.   State the Shepard's entry for the A.L.R.2d annotation that cited *Borden*.

12a.   Did the A.L.R. reference in the previous question appear in the annotation or its supplement? If you need help with this question, refer to the prefatory material entitled *Illustrative Citations*.

13a.   If your *Shepard's United States Citations–Case Edition* includes volumes covering L. Ed. cites, find the listing for the case from Question 6 under its L. Ed. cite. What is the cite of the district court case from the Third Circuit that cited *Borden* for the issue of law covered by the tenth headnote?

14a.   If your set includes volumes covering S. Ct. cites, find the listings for the case from Question 6 under its S. Ct. cite. What court of appeals opinion from the Fifth Circuit cited a point of law from West headnote number 5 of your case?

SECTION II: Complete the Questions 1b-14b in section II, if your library does NOT have the Shepard's volumes in print. Use Shepard's online.

CITATION RULES: When a case cite appears in your answers, use the standard abbreviation for the reporter as found in *The Bluebook: A Uniform System of Citation*, 17th ed., give the first page of the citing case, and give the pinpoint cite to the page on which the case you are Shepardizing is cited.

Questions 1b-5b require you to Shepardize the same case you worked with in Assignments Three and Four: *Adamson v. Hill*, 449 P.2d 536 (Kan. 1969). Logon to http://www.lexisnexis.com/shepards/ or http://www.lexisnexis.com/lawschool/

1b.   Shepardize the case. What is its parallel cite to the official reporter?

2b.   Has a 1972 Colorado case cited the *Adamson* case? If so, state its regional cite.

3b.   What is the cite of the 1976 decision that distinguished the *Adamson* case?

4b.   Has a 31 A.L.R.3d annotation cited *Adamson*? If so, state the cite.

5b.   In law practice, you might want to read some or all of the cases that have cited your case. Click on the link to the case in your answer to Question 2. Does this case concern asserting res judicata as collateral estoppel?

Now, you will Shepardize the case *United States v. Borden Co.*, 308 U.S. 188. Custom Restrictions in Shepard's online allows you to limit your citing references by analysis, jurisdiction, headnote and date. Use Custom Restrictions to help you find the following cases:

6b.   What are the parallel cites to *West's Supreme Court Reporter* and *U.S. Supreme Court Reports, Lawyers' Edition*?

7b.   In the prior history, what is the cite of the same case in federal district court?

8b.   What is the cite of the 1960 court of appeals case from the Ninth Circuit that explained the *Borden* case?

9b.   What is the cite of the 1980 Missouri decision that cited the *Borden* case?

10b.   What 1983 Fourth Circuit court of appeals case's dissent cited *Borden*?

11b.   State the Shepard's entry for the 20 A.L.R. Fed. annotation that cited *Borden*.

12b.   Did the A.L.R. reference in the previous question appear in the annotation or its supplement?

13b.   What is the cite of the 1962 district court case from the Third Circuit that cited *Borden* for the issue of law covered by the tenth headnote in the L. Ed. version of the *Borden* case?

14b.   What 1959 court of appeals opinion from the Fifth Circuit cited a point of law from *West's Supreme Court Reporter* headnote number 5 of your case?

Reshelve or logoff Shepard's and find the *National Reporter Blue Book*.

15.   You can also locate the regional cite to a case if you have the official cite by using the *National Reporter Blue Book*. Use the *National Reporter Blue Book* and state the unofficial parallel cites for the official cites listed below. Abbreviate the names of the unofficial reporters according to *The Bluebook: A Uniform System of Citation*. Note: The set contains many volumes, organized in rough chronological order. Be certain that you use the volume that includes the official cite to your case. The date given with each cite will help.

        a.   145 Ohio 194 (1945)

        b.   176 Conn. 421 (1979)

ASSIGNMENT FIVE
UPDATING CASES–SHEPARD'S CITATIONS
EXERCISE C

GOAL OF THIS ASSIGNMENT:
**To teach you how to identify a parallel cite, case history, and case treatment in a
   Shepard's entry either in paper or online.**
To show you the usefulness of the *National Reporter Blue Book*.

**SECTION I: Complete Questions 1a-14a in Section I if your library has the
   Shepard's volumes available in print.**

CITATION RULES: When a case cite appears in your answers, use the standard
   abbreviation for the reporter as found in *The Bluebook: A Uniform System of
   Citation*, 17th ed. It may differ substantially from the Shepard's abbreviation.

**Questions 1a-4a require you to Shepardize the same case you worked with
in Assignments Three and Four: *Auric v. Cont'l Cas. Co.*, 331 N.W.2d 325
(Wis. 1983). Find the case in the <u>bound</u> *Shepard's Northwestern Citations*
volumes that contain cites to it.**

1a.   Shepardize the case. What is its parallel cite?

2a.   Has an Iowa case cited the *Auric* case? If so, state its cite as listed in Shepard's.
        Remember, Shepard's in print does not list the first page of the case, but only the
        actual page that cites your case.

3a.   What is the cite of the decision that explained the *Auric* case?

4a.   Have any A.L.R.4th annotations cited *Auric*? If so, state the **second listed** cite.

Reshelve Shepard's Citations.

5a.   Look up the case in your answer to Question 2. Does this case concern a cause
        of action by a will beneficiary against the testator's attorney?

Now, you will Shepardize a U.S. Supreme Court case, *Moser v. United States*, 341 U.S. 41, 71 S. Ct. 553, 95 L. Ed. 729. Examine the spine of *Shepard's United States Citations–Case Edition*, Volumes 1.1 - 1.10 and find the volume in which your case appears to answer Questions 6a - 14a.

6a.   How does Shepard's show parallel cites?

7a.   What is the cite of the same case in federal district court?

8a.   What is the cite of the court of appeals case from the Ninth Circuit that explained the *Moser* case?

9a.   What is the cite of the **third listed** Pennsylvania decision that cited *Moser*?

10a.   What Third Circuit court of appeals case's dissent cited *Moser*?

11a.   State the Shepard's entry for the A.L.R.2d annotation that cited *Moser*.

12a.   Did the A.L.R. reference in the previous question appear in the annotation or its supplement? If you need help with this question, refer to the preface.

13a.   If your *Shepard's United States Citations–Case Edition* includes volumes covering L. Ed. cites, find the listing for the case from Question 6 under its L. Ed. cite. What is the cite of the court of appeals case from the First Circuit that cited *Moser* for the issue of law covered by the second headnote?

14a.   If your set includes volumes covering S. Ct. cites, find the listings for the case from Question 6 under its S. Ct. cite. What district court opinion from the Eighth Circuit cited a point of law from West headnote number 3 of your case?

SECTION II: Complete the Questions 1b-14b in section II, if your library does NOT have the Shepard's volumes in print. Use Shepard's online.

CITATION RULES: When a case cite appears in your answers, use the standard abbreviation for the reporter as found in *The Bluebook: A Uniform System of Citation*, 17th ed., give the first page of the citing case, and give the pinpoint cite to the page on which the case you are Shepardizing is cited.

Questions 1b-5b require you to Shepardize the same case you worked with in Assignments Three and Four: *Auric v. Cont'l Cas. Co.*, 331 N.W.2d 325 (Wis. 1983). Logon to http://www.lexisnexis.com/shepards/ or http://www.lexisnexis.com/lawschool/.

1b.   Shepardize the case. What is its parallel cite to the official reporter?

2b.   Has a 1987 Iowa case cited the *Auric* case? If so, state its cite.

3b.   Click on the link to the case in your answer to Question 2. Does this case concern a cause of action by a will beneficiary against the testator's attorney?

4b.   What is the regional 1987 cite of the decision that explained the *Auric* case?

5b.   Have any 61 A.L.R.4th annotation cited *Auric*? If so, state the **first listed** cite.

Now, you will Shepardize the case *Moser v. United States*, 341 U.S. 41. Custom Restrictions in Shepard's online allows you to limit your citing references by analysis, jurisdiction, headnote and date. Use Custom Restrictions to help you find the following cases:

6b.   What are the parallel cites to *West's Supreme Court Reporter* and *U.S. Supreme Court Reports, Lawyers' Edition*?

7b.   In the prior history, what is the cite of the same case in federal district court?

8b.   What is the cite of the 1978 court of appeals case from the Ninth Circuit that explained the *Moser* case?

9b.   What is the regional cite of the **1962** Pennsylvania decision that cited *Moser*?

10b.   What 1983 Third Circuit court of appeals case's dissent cited *Moser*?

11b.   State the Shepard's entry for the 1 A.L.R.2d annotation that cited *Moser*.

12b.   Did the A.L.R. reference in the previous question appear in the annotation or its supplement?

13b.   What is the cite of the 1955 court of appeals case from the First Circuit that cited *Moser* for the issue of law covered by the second headnote in the L. Ed. version of the *Moser* case?

14b.   What 1959 district court opinion from the Eighth Circuit cited a point of law from *West's Supreme Court Reporter* headnote number 3 of your case?

Reshelve or logoff Shepard's and find the *National Reporter Blue Book*.

15.   You can also locate the regional cite to a case if you have the official cite by using the *National Reporter Blue Book*. Use the *National Reporter Blue Book* and state the unofficial parallel cites for the official cites listed below. Abbreviate the names of the unofficial reporters according to *The Bluebook: A Uniform System of Citation*. Note: The set contains many volumes, organized in rough chronological order. Be certain that you use the volume that includes the official cite to your case. The date given with each cite will help.

            a. 276 Minn. 245 (1967)

            b. 267 Or. 94 (1973)

ASSIGNMENT FIVE
UPDATING CASES–SHEPARD'S CITATORS
EXERCISE D

GOAL OF THIS ASSIGNMENT:
To teach you how to identify a parallel cite, case history, and case treatment in a
Shepard's entry either in paper or online.
To show you the usefulness of the *National Reporter Blue Book*.

SECTION I: Complete Questions 1a-14a in Section I if your library has the
Shepard's volumes available in print.

CITATION RULES: When a case cite appears in your answers, use the standard
abbreviation for the reporter as found in *The Bluebook: A Uniform System of
Citation*, 17th ed. It may differ substantially from the Shepard's abbreviation.

Questions 1a-4a require you to Shepardize the same case you worked with
in Assignments Three and Four: *Stewart v. Williams*, 255 S.E.2d 699 (Ga.
1979). Find the case in the <u>bound</u> *Shepard's Southeastern Citations* volumes
that contain cites to it.

1a.   Shepardize the case. What is its parallel cite?

2a.   Has a North Dakota case cited the *Stewart* case? If so, state its cite as listed in
        Shepard's. Remember, Shepard's in print does not list the first page of the case,
        but only the actual page that cites your case.

3a.   What is the cite of the decision that explained the *Stewart* case?

4a.   Has an A.L.R.4th annotation cited *Stewart*? If so, state the cite for the listed one.

Reshelve Shepard's Citations.

5a.   In law practice, you might want to read some or all of the cases that have cited
        your case. Look up the case in your answer to Question 2. Does this case involve
        false imprisonment?

Now, you will Shepardize a U.S. Supreme Court case, *Smith v. Goguen*, 415 U.S. 566, 94 S. Ct. 1242, 39 L. Ed. 2d 605. Examine the spine of *Shepard's United States Citations–Case Edition*, Volumes 1.1 - 1.10 and find the volume in which your case appears to answer Questions 6a - 14a.

6a.   How does Shepard's show parallel cites?

7a.   What is the cite of the same case in federal district court?

8a.   What is the cite of the court of appeals case from the Fifth Circuit that explained the *Smith* case?

9a.   What is the cite of the Oklahoma decision that cited the *Smith* case?

10a.   What Ninth Circuit court of appeals case's dissent cited *Smith*?

11a.   State the Shepard's entry for the A.L.R.3d annotation that cited *Smith*.

12a.   Did the A.L.R. reference in the previous question appear in the annotation or its supplement? If you need help with this question, refer to the preface.

13a.   If your *Shepard's United States Citations–Case Edition* includes volumes covering L. Ed. cites, find the listing for the case from Question 6 under its L. Ed. 2d. cite. What is the cite of the court of appeals case from the Eighth Circuit that cited *Smith* for the issue of law covered by the fifth headnote?

14a.   If your set includes volumes covering S. Ct. cites, find the listings for the case from Question 6 under its S. Ct. cite. What district court opinion from the Ninth Circuit cited a point of law from West headnote number 2 of your case?

SECTION II: Complete the Questions 1b-14b in section II, if your library does NOT have the Shepard's volumes in print. Use Shepard's online.

CITATION RULES: When a case cite appears in your answers, use the standard abbreviation for the reporter as found in *The Bluebook: A Uniform System of Citation*, 17th ed., give the first page of the citing case, and give the pinpoint cite to the page on which the case you are Shepardizing is cited.

> **Questions 1b-5b require you to Shepardize the same case you worked with in Assignments Three and Four:** *Stewart v. Williams*, **255 S.E.2d 699 (Ga. 1979). Logon to http://www.lexisnexis.com/shepards/ or http://www.lexisnexis.com/lawschool/.**

1b.   Shepardize the case. What is its parallel cite to the official reporter?

2b.   Has a 1992 North Dakota case cited the *Stewart* case? If so, state its cite.

3b.   Click on the link to the case in your answer to Question 2. Does this case involve false imprisonment?

4b.   What is the regional cite of the 1983 decision that explained the *Stewart* case?

5b.   Has a 39 A.L.R.4th annotation cited *Stewart*? If so, state the cite.

> **Now, you will Shepardize the case** *Smith v. Goguen*, **415 U.S. 566. Custom Restrictions in Shepard's online allows you to limit your citing references by analysis, jurisdiction, headnote and date. Use Custom Restriction to help you find the following cases:**

6b.   What are the parallel cites to *West's Supreme Court Reporter* and *U.S. Supreme Court Reports, Lawyers' Edition* 2d?

7b.   In the prior history, what is the cite of the same case in federal district court?

8b.   What is the cite of the1978 court of appeals case from the Fifth Circuit that explained the *Smith* case?

9b.   What is the cite of the 1982 Oklahoma decision that cited the *Smith* case?

10b.   What 1975 Ninth Circuit court of appeals case's dissent cited *Smith*?

11b.   State the Shepard's entry for the 41 A.L.R.3d annotation that cited *Smith*.

12b.   Did the A.L.R. reference in the previous question appear in the annotation or its supplement?

13b.   What is the cite of the 1981 court of appeals case from the Eighth Circuit that cited *Smith* for the issue of law covered by the fifth headnote in the L. Ed. 2d version of the *Smith* case?

14b.   What 1983 federal district court opinion from the Ninth Circuit cited a point of law from *West's Supreme Court Reporter* headnote number 2 of your case?

Reshelve or logoff Shepard's and find the *National Reporter Blue Book*.

15.   You can also locate the regional cite to a case if you have the official cite by using the *National Reporter Blue Book*. Use the *National Reporter Blue Book* and state the unofficial parallel cites for the official cites listed below. Abbreviate the names of the unofficial reporters according to *The Bluebook: A Uniform System of Citation*. Note: The set contains many volumes, organized in rough chronological order. Be certain that you use the volume that includes the official cite to your case. The date given with each cite will help.

        a. 124 Colo. 106 (1951)

        b. 115 Tex. 515 (1926)

ASSIGNMENT SIX
AMERICAN LAW REPORTS
EXERCISE A

GOALS OF THIS ASSIGNMENT:
To give you practice at using the A.L.R. tables and indexes.
To find whether a relevant annotation has been superseded or supplemented.

1. Continuing the "one good case" approach, you will start with the case you have used since Assignment Three, *State v. Gilmore*, 511 A.2d 1150 (N.J. 1986). How can you use this case to get to a relevant A.L.R. annotation? Shepardize it in the bound Shepard's Atlantic, state volumes or online. What 79 A.L.R.3d annotation entry is listed in the citing references?

    Find the annotation from 79 A.L.R.3d and answer Questions 2-10.
    Remember that Shepard's will direct you to the page that cited your case.
    Go to the beginning of the annotation in the hardbound volume.

2. What is the correct citation of the annotation itself? (See Rule 16.6.5 of *The Bluebook*.)

3. Remember, the full text of an opinion precedes each annotation that explains the law in the case's subject area. State the full regional citation of the opinion whose text is printed in full.

4. Go back to the annotation. To which sections of the Am. Jur. 2d topic *Jury* could you turn to find related material?

5. Examine the Index section. Which section discusses conviction for kidnaping?

6. Examine the Table of Jurisdictions. This table will quickly tell you all jurisdictions covered by the annotation. Are any Indiana cases discussed in this annotation?

7.   Examine the scope notes and the references to related matters in the preliminary matters. State the cite of the annotation listed which discusses the exclusion of attorneys from jury list in criminal cases.

8.   Examine § 6. Note the citing of *Gilmore* in the pocket part. What 1983 Massachusetts case is cited in this section of the pocket part? State its name.

9.   Look at the beginning of the annotation in the pocket part to this volume. Examine the beginning of the updating material for a note telling you that the annotation has been superseded. Is there a note telling you that this annotation has been superseded?

10.   The pocket parts in A.L.R.3d, 4th, 5th and Fed. volumes also provide information on later cases that are relevant to the annotation. Provide the full regional citation of a 1980 Alaska Supreme Court case that updates § 3 of the annotation.

Reshelve A.L.R. and find the last volume of the A.L.R. Index.

11.   You can also tell if an annotation has been superseded by looking in the Annotation History Table, found at the end of the last A.L.R. Index volume. Has 12 A.L.R.2d 598 been superseded? If so, state the cite of the superseding annotation?

You have just used A.L.R. by the case method–starting with a relevant case that has been cited in an annotation. Use the Index to A.L.R. to find annotations by subject.

12.   Use the A.L.R. Index. State the cite of the annotation that discusses the liability of a school for injury to a student resulting from cheerleader activities.

ASSIGNMENT SIX
AMERICAN LAW REPORTS
EXERCISE B

GOALS OF THIS ASSIGNMENT:
To give you practice at using the A.L.R. tables and indexes.
To find whether a relevant annotation has been superseded or supplemented.

1. Continuing the "one good case" approach, you will start with the case you have used since Assignment Three, *Adamson v. Hill*, 449 P.2d 536 (Kan. 1969). How can you use this case to get to a relevant A.L.R. annotation? Shepardize it in the bound Shepard's Pacific, state volumes or online. What 31 A.L.R.3d annotation entry is listed in the citing references?

    Find the annotation from 31 A.L.R.3d and answer Questions 2-10.
    Remember that Shepard's will direct you to the page that cited your case.
    Go to the beginning of the annotation in the hardbound volume.

2. What is the correct citation of the annotation itself? (See Rule 16.6.5 of *The Bluebook*.)

3. Remember, the full text of an opinion accompanies each annotation that explains the law in the case's subject area. This case is referenced at the bottom of the first page of the annotation. State the full regional citation of the opinion whose text is printed in full.

4. Go back to the annotation. To which sections of the Am. Jur. 2d topic *Judgments* could you turn to find related material?

5. Examine the Index section. Which section discusses exceptions to traditional rule requiring mutuality or privity?

6. Examine the Table of Jurisdictions. This table will quickly tell you all jurisdictions covered by the annotation. Are any Nebraska cases discussed in this annotation?

7.   Examine the scope notes and the references to related matters in the prefatory matters. State the cite of the annotation listed which discusses the modern status of the doctrine of res judicata in criminal cases.

8.   Examine § 2[a]. Note the citing of *Adamson v. Hill* in footnote 11. What 1968 case from New Hampshire is cited in § 2[a] as well? State its name.

9.   Look up the cite to the annotation in the pocket part to this volume. Examine the beginning of the updating material for a note telling you that the annotation has been superseded. Is there a note telling you that this annotation has been superseded?

10.   The pocket parts in A.L.R.3d, 4th, 5th and Fed. volumes also provide information on later cases that are relevant to the annotation. Provide the full regional citation of an Arizona case that updates § 3 of the annotation.

Reshelve A.L.R. and find the last volume of the A.L.R. Index.

11.   You can also tell if an annotation has been superseded by looking in the Annotation History Table, found at the end of the last A.L.R. Index volume. Has 2 A.L.R.3d 537 been superseded? If so, state the cite of the superseding annotation?

You have just used A.L.R. by the case method–starting with a relevant case that has been cited in an annotation. Use the Index to A.L.R. to find annotations by subject.

12.   Use the A.L.R. Index. State the cite of the annotation concerning smoking as a factor in child custody and visitation cases where the child has asthma.

ASSIGNMENT SIX
AMERICAN LAW REPORTS
EXERCISE C

GOALS OF THIS ASSIGNMENT:
To give you practice at using the A.L.R. tables and indexes.
To find whether a relevant annotation has been superseded or supplemented.

1. Continuing the "one good case" approach, you will start with the case you have used since Assignment Three, *Auric v. Cont'l Cas. Co.*, 331 N.W.2d 325 (Wis. 1983). How can you use this case to get to a relevant A.L.R. annotation? Shepardize it in the bound Shepard's Northwestern, state volumes or online. What 61 A.L.R.4th annotation is listed second in paper Shepard's and listed first in online Shepard's?

   Find the annotation from 61 A.L.R.4th and answer Questions 2-10. Remember that Shepard's in print will direct you to the page that cited your case. Go to the beginning of the annotation in the hardbound volume.

2. What is the correct citation of the annotation itself? (See Rule 16.6.5 of *The Bluebook*.)

3. Remember, the full text of an opinion precedes each annotation that explains the law in the case's subject area. State the full regional citation of the opinion whose text is printed in full.

4. Go back to the annotation. To which sections of the Am. Jur. 2d topic *Attorneys at Law* could you turn to find related material?

5. Examine the Index section. Which section discusses bail hearing?

6. Examine the Table of Jurisdictions. This table will quickly tell you all jurisdictions covered by the annotation. Are any Texas cases discussed in this annotation?

7.   Examine the scope notes and the references to related matters in the preliminary matters. State the cite of the annotation listed which discusses allowance of punitive damages in action against attorney for malpractice.

8.   Examine § 5. Note the citation of the *Auric v. Cont'l Cas.* What 1969 California case is cited here as well? State its name.

9.   Look up the cite to the annotation in the pocket part to this volume. Examine the beginning of the updating material for a note telling you that the annotation has been superseded. Is there a note telling you that this annotation has been superseded?

10.   The pocket parts in A.L.R.3d, 4th, 5th and Fed. volumes also provide information on later cases that are relevant to the annotation. Provide the full regional citation of a 2000 Massachusetts Supreme Court case that updates § 8[a] of the annotation.

Reshelve A.L.R. and find the last volume of the A.L.R. Index.

11.   You can also tell if an annotation has been superseded by looking in the Annotation History Table, found at the end of the last A.L.R. Index volume. Has 92 A.L.R.2d 838 been superseded? If so, state the cite of the superseding annotation?

You have just used A.L.R. by the case method–starting with a relevant case that has been cited in an annotation. Use the Index to A.L.R. to find annotations by subject.

12.   Use the A.L.R. Index. State the cite of the annotation that discusses the liability for injury to a participant in the martial art of jujitsu.

ASSIGNMENT SIX
AMERICAN LAW REPORTS
EXERCISE D

GOALS OF THIS ASSIGNMENT:
To give you practice at using the A.L.R. tables and indexes.
To find whether a relevant annotation has been superseded or supplemented.

1. Continuing the "one good case" approach, you will start with the case you have used since Assignment Three, *Stewart v. Williams*, 255 S.E.2d 699 (Ga.1979). How can you use this case to get to a relevant A.L.R. annotation? Shepardize it in the bound Shepard's Southeastern, state volumes or online. What 39 A.L.R.4th annotation is listed in the citing references?

    Find the annotation from 39 A.L.R.4th and answer Questions 2-10.
    Remember that Shepard's will direct you to the page that cited your case.
    Go to the beginning of the annotation in the hardbound volume.

2. What is the correct citation of the annotation itself? (See Rule 16.6.5 of *The Bluebook*.)

3. Remember, the full text of an opinion precedes each annotation that explains the law in the case's subject area. State the full regional citation of the opinion whose text is printed in full.

4. Go back to the annotation. To which sections of the Am. Jur. 2d topic *False Imprisonment* could you turn to find related material?

5. Examine the Index section. Which section discusses handwriting?

6. Examine the Table of Jurisdictions. This table will quickly tell you all jurisdictions covered by the annotation. Are any Florida cases discussed in this annotation?

7. Examine the scope notes and the references to related matters in the preliminary matters. State the cite of the annotation listed which discusses a principal's liability for false arrest or imprisonment caused by agent or servant.

8. Examine § 6[a]. Note the discussion of *Stewart v. Williams*. What 1939 Iowa case is discussed here as well? State its name.

9. Look up the cite to the annotation in the pocket part to this volume. Examine the beginning of the updating material for a note telling you that the annotation has been superseded. Is there a note telling you that this annotation has been superseded?

10. The pocket parts in A.L.R.3d, 4th, 5th and Fed. volumes also provide information on later cases that are relevant to the annotation. Provide the full regional citation of a 1986 Oregon case that updates § 6[b] of the annotation.

Reshelve A.L.R. and find the last volume of the A.L.R. Index.

11. You can also tell if an annotation has been superseded by looking in the Annotation History Table, found at the end of the last A.L.R. Index volume. Has 22 A.L.R.4th183 been superseded? If so, state the cite of the superseding annotation?

You have just used A.L.R. by the case method–starting with a relevant case that has been cited in an annotation. Use the Index to A.L.R. to find annotations by subject.

12. Use the A.L.R. Index. State the cite of the annotation concerning undue influence in a non-testamentary gift to a spiritual adviser.

ASSIGNMENT SEVEN
REVIEW--FINDING, CITING AND UPDATING CASES
EXERCISE A

GOALS OF THIS ASSIGNMENT:
To review the use of digests, Shepard's in print or online and A.L.R. to find cases.
To combine several steps of a research strategy using different types of materials.
Use the *Federal Practice Digest 4th* for Questions 1-3.

Assume that you are an attorney representing a software development company whose competitor is claiming that your client infringed on its copyright on a particular program. You want to file a motion for summary judgment in this matter since based on expert testimony and analytic dissection, you do believe the substantial similarity test will be met. You need to research and find case law on point.

1. Can you find a case on point? The subject is governed by federal law. Use the *Federal Practice Digest 4th*. Start with the Descriptive Word Index to find your topic and key number, then go to the topic volume. Find a 1992 case from the Ninth Circuit Court of Appeals arising out of California that appears relevant. Provide the full citation for the case.

2. Under what topic and key number did you find the case?

3. Before you leave the digest, **update your digest search by looking in the pocket part or cumulative supplement**. Look under the key number from Question 2. Find a 1999 Eleventh Circuit Court of Appeals case arising out of Florida concerning summary judgment in a copyright infringement case where a reasonable jury could not find the two works substantially similar. Provide the full citation of the court of appeals case.

Find the case from Question 1.

4.   Given your fact situation, is this case on point?

5.   Which headnote specifically discusses that the district court properly used analytic dissection on motion for summary judgment? List its number, e.g., first, second, third, etc.

6.   Which judge wrote the opinion in this case?

7.   If your case was coming to trial in federal district court in Texas, would this case be mandatory authority?

8.   Examine the case. Which rule of the Federal Rules of Civil Procedure explicitly authorizes the district court to protect parties from "undue burden or expense" in discovery by ordering "that a trade or other confidential information not be disclosed or be disclosed only in a designated way."

9.   Did the court of appeals decide that in applying the intrinsic test, that "analytic dissection and expert testimony are not appropriate"?

10. In what 1977 case did the Ninth Circuit Court of Appeals hold that in assessing the similarity of two works, expert testimony is appropriate in some respects and inappropriate in others? State the name of the case, as listed in the opinion.

Questions 11a-14a: Use Shepard's print edition. If your library does not have the Shepard's in print, answer Questions 11b-16b online.

> **Now update the Court of Appeals case from Question 1, by Shepardizing it in the bound main volumes (do not use the Supplements).**

11a.   Look at the front of the Shepard's at the "History and Treatment Abbreviations" on the inside cover of the volume. Study the abbreviations for case history. Now find the listing for the cite to your case. Is there any prior or subsequent case history listed? If so, state the cite.

12a.   Note that your case has been cited in two Fifth Circuit cases. State the **first listed** cite as found in Shepard's.

13a.   What is the reference to the A.L.R. Fed. annotation that has cited your case?

14a.   One case you might want to read is the First Circuit federal district case that cited your case. What is the cite of the case as found in Shepard's?

> **Look up the case from Question 14a.**

15a.   What is the name of the case?

16a.   Is the case relevant to the issue of summary judgment in a copyright infringement action?

Questions 11b-16b: Use Shepard's online. If your library has Shepard's in print, answer Questions 11a-16a.
Go to either http://www.lexisnexis.com/shepards/ or http://www.lexisnexis.com/lawschool/ to Shepardize the case from Question 1. When citing to a case, provide the volume, reporter, first page of the case, and the page on which your case was cited.

11b.   Using Shepard's online, locate the cite for the appeal after remand in the subsequent history. Provide the volume, reporter and page number.

12b.   What is the cite of the 1994 Fifth Circuit Court of Appeals case arising out of Texas that has cited your case?

13b.   What is the reference to the A.L.R. Fed. annotation that has cited your case?

14b.   One case you might want to read is the 1992 First Circuit federal district case that followed your case. What is the cite of the case?

15b.   Click on the name of the case from Question 14b. What is the docket number of the case?

16b.   Is the case relevant to the issue of summary judgment in a copyright infringement action?

Now, find the print version of the 119 A.L.R. Fed. annotation you found in Question 13a or 13b.

17.   What is the full citation to the annotation, in correct *Bluebook* form according to Rule 16.6.5?

18.   Find where the *Brown Bag Software* case is cited in § 8 of the annotation. Is this A.L.R. Fed. annotation relevant to our issue?

ASSIGNMENT SEVEN
REVIEW--FINDING, CITING AND UPDATING CASES
EXERCISE B

GOALS OF THIS ASSIGNMENT:
To review the use of digests, Shepard's in print or online and A.L.R. to find cases.
To combine several steps of a research strategy using different types of materials.
Use the *Federal Practice Digest 4th* for Questions 1-3.

Assume that you are an attorney representing a college sophomore who was convicted of conspiring with his three roommates, two dorm neighbors and his girlfriend to conduct an illegal gambling business out of his dorm room from January 2003 to April 2003 in violation of federal law. You believe that the government's evidence was not sufficient to support a conspiracy conviction for gambling. You need to research and find case law on point.

1.   Can you find a case on point? Certain crimes are governed by federal law resulting in criminal trials in federal courts. Use the *Federal Practice Digest 4th*. Start with the Descriptive Word Index to find your topic and key number, then go to the topic volume. Find a 1988 case from the Ninth Circuit Court of Appeals arising out of California that appears relevant. Provide the full citation for the case.

2.   Under what topic and key number did you find the case?

3.   Before you leave the digest, **update your digest search by looking in the pocket part or supplementary pamphlet**. Look under the key number from Question 2. Find a 1997 Tenth Circuit Court of Appeals case arising out of Oklahoma concerning sufficiency of evidence to establish gambling conspiracy. Provide the full citation of the case.

Find the case from Question 1.

4.   Given your fact situation, is this case on point?

5.   Which headnote specifically discusses that testimony regarding various individuals' involvement in gambling business was sufficient to uphold finding that defendants contemplated involvement of five or more persons in gambling operation so as to sustain a conviction of conspiracy to conduct illegal gambling business? List its number, e.g., first, second, third, etc.

6.   Which judge wrote the opinion in this case?

7.   If your case was coming to trial in federal district court in Texas, would this case be mandatory authority?

8.   Examine the case. Count One of the indictment stated that Gilley and Rodriguez conspired to conduct an illegal gambling business in violation of what federal statute?

9.   According to the opinion, must proof of the conspiratorial agreement be made by direct evidence?

10.   What 1959 United States Supreme Court case did the court cite that held that proof must show that the alleged conspirators agreed to engage in acts, which if consummated, would constitute an offense against the United States? State the name of the case, as it is listed in the opinion.

Questions 11a-14a: Use Shepard's print edition. If your library does not have the Shepard's in print, answer questions 11b-16b online.
Now update the Court of Appeals case from Question 1, by Sheparizing it in the main bound volumes (do not use the Supplements).

11a.   Look at the front of the Shepard's at the "History and Treatment Abbreviations" on the inside cover of the volume. Study the abbreviations for case history. Now find the listing for the cite to your case. Is there any prior or subsequent case history listed? If so, state the cite(s).

12a.   Note that your case has been cited by a Tenth Circuit case. State its cite as found in Shepard's.

13a.   What are the references to the A.L.R. Fed. annotation that have cited your case?

14a.   One case you might want to read is the Second Circuit federal district case that cited your case. What is the cite of the case as found in Shepard's?

Look up the case from Question 14a.

15a.   What is the name of the case?

16a.   Is it relevant to the issue of sufficiency of evidence to prove conspiracy in a gambling case?

Questions 11b-16b: Use Shepard's online. If your library has Shepard's in print, answer Questions 11a-16a.
Go to either http://www.lexisnexis.com/shepards/ or http://www.lexisnexis.com/lawschool/ to Shepardize the case from Question 1. When citing to a case, provide the volume, reporter, first page of the case, and the page on which your case was cited.

11b.   Using Shepard's online, locate the cite where the U.S. Supreme Court has denied cert. List the S. Ct. cite by providing the volume, reporter and page number.

12b.   What is the cite of the 1988 Tenth Circuit Court of Appeals case that distinguished your case?

13b.   What are the references to the A.L.R. Fed. annotations that have cited your case?

14b.   One case you might want to read is the 1994 Second Circuit federal district case that cited your case. What is the cite of the case?

15b.   Click on the name of the case from Question 14b. What is the docket number of the case?

16b.   Is the case relevant to the issue of sufficiency of evidence to prove conspiracy in a gambling case?

Now, find the print version of the 21 A.L.R. Fed. annotation you found in Question 13a or 13b.

17.   What is the full citation to the annotation, in correct *Bluebook* form according to Rule 16.6.5?

18.   Find where the *Gilley* case is cited in the pocket part. Is it cited here for the discussion of sufficiency of evidence to prove conspiracy in a gambling case?

ASSIGNMENT SEVEN
REVIEW--FINDING, CITING AND UPDATING CASES
EXERCISE C

GOALS OF THIS ASSIGNMENT:
To review the use of digests, Shepard's in print or online and A.L.R. to find cases.
To combine several steps of a research strategy using different types of materials.
Use the *Federal Practice Digest 4th* for Questions 1-3.

Assume that you are an attorney representing a widow whose spouse was fatally injured in a fire at a Texas fireworks factory. The deceased had been a new employee at the factory and had recently been fitted with a safety suit which he was wearing at the time of the accident. Your client contends that her husband was never warned or instructed in the proper use of the safety suit. You are going to bring a products liability suit against the Michigan manufacturer of the suit and the Louisiana distributor of the suit. You need to research cases dealing with whether inadequate warning and instruction can render a product defective even if the product had no manufacturing or design defects.

1.   Can you find a case on point? The lawsuit will be filed in federal court. Use the *Federal Practice Digest 4th*. Start with the Descriptive Word Index to find your topic and key number, then go to the topic volume. Find a 1986 case from the Fifth Circuit Court of Appeals arising out of Texas that appears relevant. Provide the full citation for the case.

2.   Under what topic and key number did you find the case?

3.   Before you leave the digest, **update your digest search by looking in the pocket part or cumulative supplement**. Look under the key number from Question 2. Find a 1999 Fifth Circuit Court of Appeals case arising out of Texas concerning a manufacturer's failure to warn. Provide the full citation of the case.

Find the case from Question 1.

4.   Given your fact situation, is this case on point?

5.   Which headnote specifically states that the absence of adequate warning or directions may render product defective and unreasonably dangerous, even if product has no manufacturing or design defect? List its number, e.g., first, second, third, etc.

6.   Which judge wrote the opinion in this case?

7.   If your case was coming to trial in federal district court in California, would this case be mandatory authority?

8.   Examine the case. On what date did the district court dismiss with prejudice all the third-party actions, based on the two-year statute of limitations?

9.   Is a component part manufacturer protected from liability when a defective condition results from the integration of the part into another product and the component part is free from defect?

10.   When reviewing a ruling on a directed verdict motion, the court applies the test enunciated in what case? State the name of the case, as it is listed in the opinion.

Questions 11a-14a: Use Shepard's print edition. If your library does not have the Shepard's in print, answer questions 11b-16b online.
   Now update the Court of Appeals case from Question 1, by Shepardizing it in the bound main volumes (do not use the Supplements).

11a.   Look at the front of the Shepard's at the "History and Treatment Abbreviations" on the inside cover of the volume. Study the abbreviations for case history. Now find the listing for the cite to your case. Is there any prior or subsequent case history listed? If so, state the cite.

12a.   Note that your case has been cited by a Ninth Circuit case. State its cite as found in Shepard's.

13a.   What is the reference to the A.L.R. Fed. annotation that has cited your case?

14a.   One case you might want to read is the Sixth Circuit federal district case that cited your case. What is the cite of the case as found in Shepard's?

Look up the case from Question 14a.

15a.   What is the name of the case?

16a.   Is it relevant to the issue that inadequate warnings may render a product defective?

Questions 11b-16b: Use Shepard's online. If your library has Shepard's in print, answer Questions 11a-16a.

> Go to either http://www.lexisnexis.com/shepards/ or http://www.lexisnexis.com/lawschool/ to Shepardize the case from Question 1. **When citing to a case, provide the volume, reporter, first page of the case, and the page on which your case was cited.**

11b.   Using Shepard's online, locate the cite that gives subsequent appellate history. Provide the volume, reporter and page number.

12b.   Note that your case has been cited by the 1989 Ninth Circuit Court of Appeals case. State the citation.

13b.   What is the reference to the 52 A.L.R. Fed. annotation that has cited your case?

14b.   One case you might want to read is the 1992 Sixth Circuit federal district case that followed your case. What is the cite of the case?

15b.   Click on the name of the case in Question 14b. What is the docket number of the case?

16b.   Is the case relevant to the issue that inadequate warnings may render a product defective?

Now, find the print version of the 52 A.L.R. Fed. annotation you found in Question 13a or 13b.

17.   What is the full citation to the annotation, in correct *Bluebook* form according to Rule 16.6.5?

18.   Find where the *Koonce* case is cited in the pocket part. Is it cited here for the proposition that inadequate warnings can cause a product to be defective?

ASSIGNMENT SEVEN
REVIEW--FINDING, CITING AND UPDATING CASES
EXERCISE D

GOALS OF THIS ASSIGNMENT:
To review the use of digests, Shepard's in print or online and A.L.R. to find cases.
To combine several steps of a research strategy using different types of materials.
Use the *Federal Practice Digest 4th* for Questions 1-3.

Assume that you are an attorney representing a senior vice-president of a national video rental chain. Your client is seeking compensation for overtime hours worked. She is required to work 40 hours per week but is paid on a salaried basis. However, her compensation is subject to reduction if she works less than eight hour days. She contends that this pay reduction converts her from a salaried employee to an hourly employee which entitles her to overtime pay. As her attorney, you need to research the minimum wage and overtime provisions of the Fair Labor Standards Act. One point that you want to determine is whether or not the exemptions under the law are strictly construed.

1. Can you find a case on point? The subject is governed by federal law. Use the *Federal Practice Digest 4th*. Start with the Descriptive Word Index to find your topic and key number, then go to the topic volume. Find a 1991 case from the Second Circuit Court of Appeals arising out of New York that appears relevant. Provide the full citation for the case omitting subsequent history.

2. Under what topic and key number did you find the case?

3. Before you leave the digest, **update your digest search by looking in the pocket parts or cumulative pamphlet**. Look under the key number from Question 2. Find a 2001 Eleventh Circuit Court of Appeals case arising out of Florida which states that the court of appeals would examine wage payment plans for substantial compliance with FLSA by construing remedial statutory provisions both narrowly and sensibly. Provide the full citation of the case omitting subsequent history.

Find the case from Question 1.

4.   Given your fact situation, is this case on point?

5.   Which headnote specifically states that exemptions to the Fair Labor Standards Act are to be narrowly construed, with the employer bearing the burden of proving that employees fall within exemption? List its number, e.g., first, second, third, etc.

6.   Which judge wrote the opinion in this case?

7.   If your case was coming to trial in federal district court in Texas, would this case be mandatory authority?

8.   Examine the case. Which section of 29 U.S.C. requires employers to compensate employees on a time-and-a-half basis for each hour they work in excess of the usual forty hour week?

9.   Did the court state that an employee who can be docked pay for missing a fraction of a workday must be considered an hourly employee rather than a salaried employee?

10.   In stating the well-settled law of when a district court may grant a party's motion for summary judgment, the court cited to a 1986 United States Supreme Court case. State the name of the case, as it is listed in the opinion.

Questions 11a-14a: Use Shepard's print edition. If your library does not have the Shepard's in print, answer questions 11b-16b online.
  Now update the Court of Appeals case from Question 1, by Shepardizing it in the bound main volumes (do not use the Supplements).

11a. Look at the front of the Shepard's at the "History and Treatment Abbreviations" on the inside cover of the volume. Study the abbreviations for case history. Now find the listing for the cite to your case. Is there any prior or subsequent case history listed? If so, state the cite.

12a. Note that your case has been cited by an Eighth Circuit case. State the cite as found in Shepard's.

13a. What is the cite to the A.L.R. Fed. annotation that has cited your case?

14a. One case you might want to read is the Third Circuit federal district case that cited your case. What is the cite of the case as found in Shepard's?

Look up the case from Question 14a.

15a. What is the name of the case?

16a. Is it relevant to the issue of how employee exemptions are to be construed under the Fair Labor Standards Act?

Questions 11b-16b: Use Shepard's online. If your library has Shepard's in print, answer Questions 11a-16a.

Go to either http://www.lexisnexis.com/shepards/ or http://www.lexisnexis.com/lawschool/ to Shepardize the case from Question 1. When citing to a case, provide the volume, reporter, first page of the case, and the page on which your case was cited.

11b.   Look at the prior history of your case. Locate a case which states your case is superseded by a statute. State the volume, reporter and page number.

12b.   What 1993 Eighth Circuit Court of Appeals decision explained your case.

13b.   What is the cite to the 123 A.L.R. Fed. that has cited your case?

14b.   One case you might want to read is the 1994 Third Circuit federal district case that criticized your case. What is the cite of the case?

15b.   Click on the name of the case from Question 14b. What is the docket number of the case?

16b.   Is the case relevant to the issue of how employee exemptions are to be construed under the Fair Labor Standards Act?

Now, find the print version of the 123 A.L.R. Fed. annotation you found in Question 13a or 13b.

17.   What is the full citation to the annotation, in correct *Bluebook* form according to Rule 16.6.5?

18.   Find where the *Martin* case is cited in § 8 of the annotation. Is it cited here for a discussion of Fair Labor Standards Act exemptions?

ASSIGNMENT EIGHT
FINDING AND CITING STATUTES
EXERCISE A

GOALS OF THIS ASSIGNMENT:
To acquaint you with finding federal and state statutes in your library.
To familiarize you with the rules for citing statutes in *The Bluebook: A Uniform System of Citation, 17th ed.*

CITATION RULES: You will need to read Rule 12 and Table 1 in *The Bluebook*. In this assignment we give you either a citation or a subject area and you must find federal and state statutes. Once you have found the statutes, you must cite them correctly.

The first three questions require you to find and cite a statute in the official federal code, the *United States Code* (U.S.C.). The citation includes the title number, the code abbreviation, the section number(s), the date of the code appearing on the spine, and the supplement date (if the act appears in the supplement). Include the name of the act or the act's popular name and the original uncodified section of the act if such information would aid in identification. **Example: 23 U.S.C. § 126 (2000).**

1.   For statutes currently in force, which code should you cite?

2.   What is the date of the current edition of the U.S.C.?

3.   Find and cite the *United States Code*, title 42, sections 602 to 604. Use the current edition (not the supplements). Do not include the name of the act.

The next question requires you to find and cite a statute in one of the unofficial federal codes, *United States Code Annotated* (U.S.C.A.). You may cite unofficial codes (U.S.C.A. and U.S.C.S.) when the statute is too recent to appear in the U.S.C. Include the information you used for the U.S.C., in addition to the name of the publisher. You must also include the precise location in either U.S.C.A. or U.S.C.S. where the statute appears. Cite to either the main volume, the pocket part, or both. Since no date appears on the spine of the main volume, the year cited is the copyright date. **Example: 11 U.S.C.A. § 523 (West 1993 & Supp. 2002).**

4.   Find and cite § 271 of Title 42 of U.S.C.A. correctly.

Next you must find and cite a federal session law. According to *The Bluebook*, when citing session laws, always give the name of the statute, the public law number, volume and page number of the Statutes at Large (Stat.), and year of passage if not revealed in its name. **Example: Home Energy Assistance Act of 1980, Pub. L. No. 96-223, 94 Stat. 288.**

5.   Find and cite 113 Stat. 218.

For the next two questions, find and cite a state statute in a code. We require that you use the index to find the correct act. When citing a state code, include the name of the code; the chapter, title, or other subdivision; possibly the name of the publisher; and the year of the code. **Example: Miss. Code Ann. § 75-5-109 (1999).**

6.   Use the index to the *Florida Statutes Annotated* and find a statute that defines house trailers under the Florida Uniform Traffic Control Law.

For some states, most notably California, Texas and New York, include the subject on the spine as part of the name of the code. **Example: Tex. Educ. Code Ann. § 11.055 (Vernon 1996).**

7.   Use the index to the *Annotated California Code* and find a statute stating that a city may not enact an ordinance prohibiting playing duplicate bridge.

Statutes are online on WESTLAW and LEXIS. You can search for statutes by subject area or citation. On WESTLAW, you can retrieve statutes if you have the citation with the FIND command. On LEXIS, use GET A DOCUMENT to locate statutes.

ASSIGNMENT EIGHT
FINDING AND CITING STATUTES
EXERCISE B

GOALS OF THIS ASSIGNMENT:
To acquaint you with finding federal and state statutes in your library.
To familiarize you with the rules for citing statutes in *The Bluebook: A Uniform System of Citation, 17th ed.*

CITATION RULES: You will need to read Rule 12 and Table 1 in *The Bluebook*. In this assignment we give you either a citation or a subject area and you must find federal and state statutes. Once you have found the statutes, you must cite them correctly.

The first three questions require you to find and cite a statute in the official federal code, the *United States Code* (U.S.C.). The citation includes the title number, the code abbreviation, the section number(s), the date of the code appearing on the spine, and the supplement date (if the act appears in the supplement). Include the name of the act or the act's popular name and the original uncodified section of the act if such information would aid in identification. **Example: 23 U.S.C. § 126 (2000).**

1.   For statutes currently in force, which code should you cite?

2.   What is the date of the current edition of the U.S.C.?

3.   Find and cite the *United States Code*, title 42, sections 2162 to 2166. Use the current edition (not the supplements). Do not include the name of the act.

The next question requires you to find and cite a statute in one of the unofficial federal codes, *United States Code Annotated* (U.S.C.A.). You may cite unofficial codes (U.S.C.A. and U.S.C.S.) when the statute is too recent to appear in the U.S.C. Include the information you used for the U.S.C., in addition to the name of the publisher. You must also include the precise location in either U.S.C.A. or U.S.C.S. where the statute appears. Cite to either the main volume, the pocket part, or both. Since no date appears on the spine of the main volume, the year cited is the copyright date. **Example: 22 U.S.C.A. § 4046 (West 1993 & Supp. 2002).**

4.   Find and cite § 309 of Title 44 of U.S.C.A. correctly.

Next you must find and cite a federal session law. According to *The Bluebook*, when citing session laws, always give the name of the statute, the public law number, volume and page number of the Statutes at Large (Stat.), and year of passage if not revealed in its name. **Example: Home Energy Assistance Act of 1980, Pub. L. No. 96-223, 94 Stat. 288.**

5.   Find and cite 110 Stat. 3269.

For the next two questions, find and cite a state statute in a code. We require that you use the index to locate the correct act. When citing a state code, include the name of the code; the chapter, title, or other subdivision; possibly the name of the publisher; and the year of the code. **Example: Miss. Code Ann. § 75-5-109 (1999).**

6.   Use the index to the *Code of Alabama* and find a statute requiring rifle dealers to pay a license tax.

For some states, most notably California, Texas and New York, include the subject on the spine as part of the name of the code. **Example: Cal. Penal Code § 450 (West 1999).**

7.   Use the index to the *Texas Codes Annotated* and locate a statute that defines simplified employee plans in nontestamentary transfers.

Statutes are online on WESTLAW and LEXIS. You can search for statutes by subject area or citation. On WESTLAW, you can retrieve statutes if you have the citation with the FIND command. On LEXIS, use GET A DOCUMENT to locate statutes.

ASSIGNMENT EIGHT
FINDING AND CITING STATUTES
EXERCISE C

GOALS OF THIS ASSIGNMENT:
To acquaint you with finding federal and state statutes in your library.
To familiarize you with the rules for citing statutes in *The Bluebook: A Uniform System of Citation, 17th ed.*

CITATION RULES: You will need to read Rule 12 and Table 1 in *The Bluebook*. In this assignment we give you either a citation or a subject area and you must find federal and state statutes. Once you have found the statutes, you must cite them correctly.

> The three first questions require you to find and cite a statute in the official federal code, the *United States Code* (U.S.C.). The citation includes the title number, the code abbreviation, the section number(s), the date of the code appearing on the spine, and the supplement date (if the act appears in the supplement). Include the name of the act or the act's popular name and the original uncodified section of the act if such information would aid in identification. **Example: 23 U.S.C. § 126 (2000).**

1. For statutes currently in force, which code should you cite?

2. What is the date of the current edition of the U.S.C.?

3. Find and cite the *United States Code*, title 15, sections 1062 to 1064. Use the current edition (not the supplements). Do not include the name of the act.

> The next question requires you to find and cite a statute in one of the unofficial federal codes, *United States Code Annotated* (U.S.C.A.). You may cite unofficial codes (U.S.C.A. and U.S.C.S.) when the statute is too recent to appear in the U.S.C. Include the information you used for the U.S.C., in addition to the name of the publisher. You must also include the precise location in either U.S.C.A. or U.S.C.S. where the statute appears. Cite to either the main volume, the pocket part, or both. Since no date appears on the spine of the main volume, the year cited is the copyright date. **Example: 11 U.S.C.A. § 523 (West 1993 & Supp. 2002).**

4.   Find and cite § 37 of Title 15 of U.S.C.A. correctly.

Next you must find and cite a federal session law. According to *The Bluebook*, when citing session laws, always give the name of the statute, the public law number, volume and page number of the Statutes at Large (Stat.), and year of passage if not revealed in its name. **Example: Home Energy Assistance Act of 1980, Pub. L. No. 96-223, 94 Stat. 288.**

5.   Find and cite 112 Stat. 2824.

For the next two questions, find and cite a state statute in a code. We require that you use the index to locate the correct act. When citing a state code, include the name of the code; the chapter, title, or other subdivision; possibly the name of the publisher; and the year of the code. **Example: Miss. Code Ann. § 75-5-109 (1999).**

6.   Use the index to the *Code of Laws of South Carolina* and find a statute on exempt transactions from certain laws for coin dealers and collectors where the transaction occurred at numismatic conventions.

For some states, most notably California, Texas and New York, include the subject on the spine as part of the name of the code. **Example: Tex. Educ. Code Ann. § 11.055 (Vernon 1996).**

7.   Use the index to the *Annotated California Code* and find a statute on proceedings to authenticate private records destroyed in a fire.

Statutes are online on WESTLAW and LEXIS. You can search for statutes by subject area or citation. On WESTLAW, you can retrieve statutes if you have the citation with the FIND command. On LEXIS, use GET A DOCUMENT to locate statutes.

ASSIGNMENT EIGHT
FINDING AND CITING STATUTES
EXERCISE D

GOALS OF THIS ASSIGNMENT:
To acquaint you with finding federal and state statutes in your library.
To familiarize you with the rules for citing statutes in *The Bluebook: A Uniform System of Citation, 17th ed.*

CITATION RULES: You will need to read Rule 12 and Table 1 in *The Bluebook*. In this assignment we give you either a citation or a subject area and you must find federal and state statutes. Once you have found the statutes, you must cite them correctly.

The first three questions require you to find and cite a statute in the official federal code, the *United States Code* (U.S.C.). The citation includes the title number, the code abbreviation, the section number(s), the date of the Code appearing on the spine, and the supplement date (if the act appears in the supplement). Include the name of the act or the act's popular name and the original uncodified section of the act if such information would aid in identification. **Example: 23 U.S.C. § 126 (2000).**

1. For statutes currently in force, which code should you cite?

2. What is the date of the current edition of the U.S.C.?

3. Find and cite the *United States Code*, title 10, sections 4347 to 4350. Use the current edition (not the supplements). Do not include the name of the act.

The next question requires you to find and cite a statute in one of the unofficial federal codes, *United States Code Annotated* (U.S.C.A.). You may cite unofficial codes (U.S.C.A. and U.S.C.S.) when the statute is too recent to appear in the U.S.C. Include the information you used for the U.S.C., in addition to the name of the publisher. You must also include the precise location in either U.S.C.A. or U.S.C.S. where the statute appears. Cite to either the main volume, the pocket part, or both. Since no date appears on the spine of the main volume, the year cited is the copyright date. **Example: 11 U.S.C.A. § 523 (West 1993 & Supp. 2002).**

4.   Find and cite § 1346 of Title 28 of U.S.C.A. correctly.

                        Next you must find and cite a federal session law. According to *The Bluebook*, when citing session laws, always give the name of the statute, the public law number, volume and page number of the Statutes at Large (Stat.), and year of passage if not revealed in its name. **Example: Home Energy Assistance Act of 1980, Pub. L. No. 96-223, 94 Stat. 288.**

5.   Find and cite 108 Stat. 3488.

                        For the next two questions, find and cite a state statute in a code. We require that you use the index to locate the correct act. When citing a state code, include the name of the code; the chapter, title, or other subdivision; possibly the name of the publisher; and the year of the code. **Example: Miss. Code Ann. § 75-5-109 (1999).**

6.   Use the index to the *Michigan Compiled Laws Annotated* and find a statute regulating the distribution of industrial cleaners containing phosphorus.

                        For some states, most notably California, Texas and New York, include the subject on the spine as part of the name of the code. **Example: Tex. Educ. Code Ann. § 11.055 (Vernon 1996).**

7.   Use the index to the *McKinney's Consolidated Laws of New York Annotated* or *Consolidated Laws Service* and find a statute on the motorcycle safety program.

                        Statutes are online on WESTLAW and LEXIS. On WESTLAW, you can retrieve statutes if you have the citation with the FIND command. On LEXIS, use GET A DOCUMENT to locate statutes.

ASSIGNMENT NINE
FEDERAL SESSION LAWS AND CODES
EXERCISE A

GOALS OF THIS ASSIGNMENT:
To reveal the similarities and differences between the two annotated codes.
To introduce you to federal session laws.
To introduce you to the legislative history materials available in *U.S. Code Congressional & Administrative News.*
To introduce you to the tables in one of the codes.

1.   Use the index in U.S.C.A. to find the title and section of the code to answer the following question. By what date did the Secretary of Transportation establish a national aviation noise policy? Answer the question and provide the citation to the code. Note: In *The Bluebook*, use Rule 12 and Table 1.

In your research you will seldom, if ever, use the "official" U.S. Code, because it is not current and does not contain annotations. Therefore, to answer Questions 2-7, use the two annotated codes, U.S.C.A. and U.S.C.S., of the code section you found in Question 1. **Be sure to check the pocket parts and the supplementary pamphlets for possible updates!**

2.   Look up the text of the statute from Question 1. Next, look at the information in parentheses at the end of the section. State the date, public law number, and *U.S. Statutes at Large* citation for the 1994 act passed during the 103d Congress.

3.   a.   Which code (U.S.C.A. or U.S.C.S.) refers you to the Code of Federal Regulations on Standards for aircraft type and airworthiness?
        b.   What is the citation?
                a.
                b.

4.   a.   Which code refers you to Am. Jur?

       b.   List the Am. Jur. citation.

              a.

              b.

5.   a.   Which code refers you to topic and key numbers in the American Digest System?

       b.   List the **first listed** topic and key number.

              a.

              b.

6.   a.   Which code refers you to court decisions?

       b.   State the **name** of the 1995 federal court decision.

              a.

              b.

7.   a.   Which code refers you to electronic research?

       b.   Which system do they refer you to?

              a.

              b.

Reshelve the unofficial codes.

Remember that a code is a subject arrangement of current, general laws. Note how helpful the unofficial codes can be, since they refer you to cases, encyclopedia articles, law review articles, West digests, and secondary materials.

Assume that you want to look at the text of 110 Stat. 1716.

To find the text of a law or amendment as Congress passed it, use the *U.S. Statutes at Large* for Questions 8-10.

8.   Find 110 Stat. 1716. Go to the beginning of the Public Law at 110 Stat. 1700. What is the Public Law number?

9.   What is the bill number for the act?

10.   Examine the text of the act. The approval date for most legislation is usually stated at the end of the act. When was this act approved?

Now assume that you wish to see some legislative history for this act. Legislative history refers to committee reports, legislative debates and hearings generated during the consideration of bills. Courts often consider legislative history when interpreting a statute, because legislative history can show legislative intent.

***U.S. Code Congressional & Administrative News* (U.S.C.C.A.N.) is an accessible source of legislative history and the text of public laws (Questions 11-12).**

11.   The text of the public law you already examined in *Statutes at Large* is also reprinted in U.S.C.C.A.N. in 1996, vol. 2, under 110 Stat. 1700. Look it up. On what page does the **legislative history** begin?

12.   Look up the legislative history (it is in vol. 5). Which House Report is partially reprinted?

You have now found the current text of a statute, examined the text as Congress passed it into law, and looked at some of its legislative history.

The remaining questions of this assignment require you to use the tables in the *United States Code Annotated.*

13. Use the Popular Name Table (it is in a separate volume). What is the formal name of the act commonly known as the Auto Pricing Law?

14. In your research, you will often have a session law citation or a public law number and need a code citation. Usually the best way to find this is by using the tables in the code. Use the U.S.C.A. volumes labeled "Tables Volume II" and state the U.S.C.A. title and section(s) that correspond to:

    a.   110 Stat. 3423

    b.   Pub. L. No. 102-26 § 9

You have used the two annotated codes in this assignment. In law practice, you will almost never use the official code, because it is not as often updated and it does not contain the helpful features of the annotated versions. When using the annotated codes, bear in mind they each have different features and will often contain different cases. You will want to check both if you are doing an exhaustive search for annotations.

You found a session law of your code section in the *U.S. Statutes at Large*, the official publication of federal session laws. Researchers often refer to session laws when investigating the history of a law. Session laws also appear the *U.S. Code Congressional & Administrative News*, along with legislative history. You looked up the legislative history behind your code section. When seeking legislative history, you will probably check U.S.C.C.A.N. first because using it is easier than many other sources of legislative history.

Note: Federal statutory materials are available on WESTLAW and LEXIS. Some questions in this assignment can be answered online.

ASSIGNMENT NINE
FEDERAL SESSION LAWS AND CODES
EXERCISE B

GOALS OF THIS ASSIGNMENT:
To reveal the similarities and differences between the two annotated codes.
To introduce you to federal session laws.
To introduce you to the legislative history materials available in *U.S. Code Congressional & Administrative News*.
To introduce you to the tables in one of the codes.

1. Use the index in U.S.C.A. to find the title and section of the code to answer the following question. In defining the term "lead-based paint," what commission was charged with determining whether paint with a certain level of lead was safe? Answer the question and provide the citation to the code. Note: In *The Bluebook*, use Rule 12 and Table 1.

    In your research you will seldom, if ever, use the "official" U.S. Code, because it is not current and does not contain annotations. Therefore, to answer Questions 2-7, use the two annotated codes, U.S.C.A. and U.S.C.S., of the code section you found in Question 1. **Be sure to check the pocket parts and the supplementary pamphlets for possible updates!**

2. Look up the text of the statute from Question 1. Next, look at the information in parentheses at the end of the section. State the date, public law number, and *U.S. Statutes at Large* citation reference for the 1971 original act.

3. a. Which code (U.S.C.A. or U.S.C.S.) refers you to legislative reports?
    b. List the page number in the U.S. Code Cong. and Adm. News for the 1971 act.
        a.
        b.

4.　a.　　Which codes refer you to topic and key numbers in the American Digest System?

　b.　　What topic and key numbers deal with disbursement of federal funds to state and local agencies?

　　　　　a.

　　　　　b.

5.　a.　　Which code refers you to the Code of Federal Regulations?

　b.　　State the titles and parts.

　　　　　a.

　　　　　b.

6.　a.　　Which code cites to C.J.S.?

　b.　　What is the citation of the C.J.S. on statutory regulation of poisons?

　　　　　a.

　　　　　b.

7.　a.　　Which codes contain annotations of court decisions?

　b.　　State the **name** of a 1993 federal case.

　　　　　a.

　　　　　b.

Reshelve the unofficial codes.

Remember that a code is a subject arrangement of current, general laws. Note how helpful the unofficial codes (U.S.C.A. and U.S.C.S.) can be, since they refer you to cases, encyclopedia articles, law review articles, West digests, and secondary materials.

Now assume that you want to look at the text of 108 Stat. 395.

To find the text of a law or amendment as Congress passed it, use the *U.S. Statutes at Large* for Questions 8-10.

8.   Find 108 Stat. 395. Go to the beginning of the Public Law at 108 Stat. 382. What is the Public Law number?

9.   What is the bill number for the act?

10.   Examine the text of the act. The approval date for most legislation is usually stated at the end of an act. When was this act approved?

Now assume that you wish to see some legislative history for this act. Legislative history refers to committee reports, legislative debates and hearings generated during the consideration of bills. Courts often consider legislative history when interpreting a statute, because legislative history can show legislative intent.

***U.S. Code Congressional & Administrative News* (U.S.C.C.A.N.) is an accessible source of legislative history and the text of public laws (Questions 11-12).**

11.   The text of the act you already examined in 108 Stat. 382 is also reprinted in U.S.C.C.A.N. in 1994, vol. 1. Look it up. On what page does the **legislative history** begin?

12.   Look up the legislative history (it is in vol. 4). Which Senate Report is reprinted?

You have now found the current text of a statute, examined the text as Congress passed it into law, and looked at some of its legislative history.

The last remaining questions of this assignment require you to use the tables in the *United States Code Annotated*.

13. Use the Popular Name Table (it is in a separate volume). What is the formal name of the act commonly known as Baby Bonds?

14. In your research, you will often have a session law citation or public law number and need a code citation. Usually the best way to find this is by using the tables in the code. Use the U.S.C.A. volumes labeled "Tables Volume I" and state the U.S.C.A. title and section that correspond to:

    a.   79 Stat. 344

    b.   Pub. L. No. 88-590 § 4

You have used the two annotated codes in this assignment. In law practice, you will almost never use the official code, because it is not as often updated and it does not contain the helpful features of the annotated versions. When using the annotated codes, bear in mind they each have different features and will often contain different cases. You will want to check both if you are doing an exhaustive search for annotations.

You found a session law of your code section in the *U.S. Statutes at Large*, the official publication of federal session laws. Researchers often refer to session laws when investigating the history of a law. Session laws also appear the *U.S. Code Congressional & Administrative News*, along with legislative history. You looked up the legislative history behind your code section. When seeking legislative history, you will probably check U.S.C.C.A.N. first because using it is easier than many other sources of legislative history.

Note: Federal statutory materials are available on WESTLAW and LEXIS. Some questions in this assignment can be answered online.

GOALS OF THIS ASSIGNMENT:
To reveal the similarities and differences between the two annotated codes.
To introduce you to federal session laws.
To introduce you to the legislative history materials available in *U.S. Code Congressional & Administrative News*.
To introduce you to the tables in one of the code.

1. Use the index in U.S.C.A. to find the title and section of the code to answer the following question. Is the purpose of the Age Discrimination Act of 1975 to prohibit age discrimination in programs receiving federal financial assistance? Answer the question and provide the citation to the code. Note: In *The Bluebook*, use Rule12 and Table 1.

    In your research you will seldom, if ever, use the "official" U.S. Code, because it is not current and does not contain annotations. Therefore, to answer Questions 2-7, use the two annotated codes, U.S.C.A. and U.S.C.S., of the code section you found in Question 1. **Be sure to check the pocket parts and the supplementary pamphlets for possible updates!**

2. Look up the text of the statute from Question 1. Next, look at the information in parentheses at the end of the section. State the date, public law number, and *U.S. Statutes at Large* citation for the 1975 act.

3. a.   Which code (U.S.C.A. or U.S.C.S.) refers you to a relevant West topic and key numbers in the American Digest System?
    b.   List the topic and key numbers.
             a.
             b.

4.   a.   Which code refers you to the Code of Federal Regulations for the Tennessee Valley Authority - Nondiscrimination with respect to age??

      b.   List the citation (volume and part).

           a.

           b.

5.   a.   Which codes refer you to law review articles?

      b.   Who is the **author** of the 1986 article that appeared in the Boston University Law Review?

           a.

           b.

6.   a.   Which code refers you to C.J.S.?

      b.   List the C.J.S. citation.

           a.

           b.

7.   a.   Which code contains annotations of court decisions?

      b.   State the **name** of the 1995 federal district court case from Maine.

           a.

           b.

Reshelve the unofficial codes.

Remember that a code is a subject arrangement of current, general laws. Note how helpful the unofficial codes (U.S.C.A. and U.S.C.S.) can be, since they refer you to cases, encyclopedia articles, law reviews, and West digests.

Now assume that you want to look at the text of 109 Stat. 84.

To find the text of a law or amendment as Congress passed it, use the *U.S. Statutes at Large* for Questions 8-10.

8. Find 109 Stat. 84. Go to the beginning of the Public Law at 109 Stat. 73. What is the Public Law number?

9. What is the bill number for the act?

10. Examine the text of the act. The approval date for most legislation is usually stated at the end of the act. When was this act approved?

Now assume that you wish to see some legislative history for this act. Legislative history refers to committee reports, legislative debates and hearings generated during the consideration of bills. Courts often consider legislative history when interpreting a statute, because legislative history can show legislative intent.

***U.S. Code Congressional & Administrative News* (U.S.C.C.A.N.) is an accessible source of legislative history and the text of public laws (Questions 11-12).**

11. The text of the public law you already examined in 109 Stat. 73 is also reprinted in U.S.C.C.A.N. in 1995, vol. 1. Look it up. Where does it direct you to look for the **legislative history**?

12. Look up the legislative history (it is in vol. 1). Which House Conference report is partially reprinted?

You have now found the current text of a statute, examined the text as Congress passed it into law, and looked at some of its legislative history.

The last remaining questions of this assignment require you to use the tables in the *United States Code Annotated.*

13. Use the Popular Name Table (it is in a separate volume). What is the formal name of the act commonly known as the Safe Streets Law of 1968?

14. In real life, you will often have a session law citation or public law number and need a code citation. Usually the best way to find this is by using the tables in the code. Use the U.S.C.A. volumes labeled "Tables Volume I." State the U.S.C.A. title and section(s) that correspond to:

    a. 63 Stat. 157

    b. Pub. L. No. 93-319 § 8

You have used the two annotated codes in this assignment. In law practice, you will almost never use the official code, because it is not as often updated and it does not contain the helpful features of the annotated versions. When using the annotated codes, bear in mind they each have different features and will often contain different cases. You will want to check both if you are doing an exhaustive search for annotations.

You found a session law of your code section in the *U.S. Statutes at Large*, the official publication of federal session laws. Researchers often refer to session laws when investigating the history of a law. Session laws also appear the *U.S. Code Congressional & Administrative News*, along with legislative history. You looked up the legislative history behind your code section. When seeking legislative history, you will probably check U.S.C.C.A.N. first because using it is easier than many other sources of legislative history.

Note: Federal statutory materials are available on WESTLAW and LEXIS. Some questions in this assignment can be answered online.

GOALS OF THIS ASSIGNMENT:

To reveal the similarities and differences between the two annotated codes.
To introduce you to federal session laws.
To introduce you to the legislative history materials available in *U.S. Code Congressional & Administrative News.*
To introduce you to the tables in one of the codes.

---

1. Use the index in U.S.C.A. to find the title and section of the code to answer the following question. What is the definition of "digital audio copied recording" under the copyright laws? Answer the question and provide the citation to the code. Note: In *The Bluebook*, use Rule 12 and Table 1.

   In your research you will seldom, if ever, use the "official" U.S. Code, because it is not current and does not contain annotations. Therefore, to answer Questions 2-7, use the two annotated codes, U.S.C.A. and U.S.C.S., of the code section you found in Question 1. **Be sure to check the pocket parts and the supplementary pamphlets for possible updates!**

2. Look up the text of the statute from Question 1. Next, look at the information in parentheses at the end of the section. State the date, public law number, and *U.S. Statutes at Large* citation for the 1992 act.

3. a. Which code (U.S.C.A. or U.S.C.S.) refers you to legislative reports?
   b. List the page number in the U.S. Code Cong. and Adm. News to which you are referred to the 1992 House Report.
      a.
      b.

117

4. a. Which code refers you to a topic and key numbers in the American Digest System?
    b.   List the **first listed** topic and key number.
         a.
         b.

5. a. Which code provides references C.J.S.?
    b. State the C.J.S. citation to "What May be Copyrighted: Sound Recordings."
         a.
         b.

6. a. Which codes provide references to law reviews?
    b. State the name of the author of the 1998 article that appeared in the Journal of the Copyright Society.
         a.
         b.

7. a. Which codes contain annotations of court decisions?
    b. State the **name** of the 1999 9th Circuit case.
         a.
         b.

Reshelve the unofficial codes.

Remember that a code is a subject arrangement of current, general laws. Note how helpful the unofficial codes (U.S.C.A. and U.S.C.S.) can be, since they refer you to cases, encyclopedia articles, law review articles, West digests, and secondary materials.

Now assume that you want to look at the text of 107 Stat. 2311.

To find the text of a law or amendment as Congress passed it, you can use *U.S. Statutes at Large* for Questions 8-10.

8. Find 107 Stat. 2311. Go back to the beginning of the Public Law at 107 Stat. 2304. What is the Public Law number?

9. What is the bill number for the act?

10. Examine the text of the act. The approval date for most legislation is usually stated at the end of the act. On what date was this act approved?

Now assume that you wish to see some legislative history for this act. Legislative history refers to committee reports, legislative debates and hearings generated during the consideration of bills. Courts often consider legislative history when interpreting a statute, because legislative history can show legislative intent.

U.S. Code Congressional & Administrative News (U.S.C.C.A.N.) is an accessible source of legislative history and the text of public laws (Questions 11-12).

11. The text of the public laws that you already examined in 107 Stat. 2304 are also reprinted in U.S.C.C.A.N. in1993 vol. 2 under Public Law 103-198. Look it up. On what page does the **legislative history** begin?

12. Look up the legislative history (it is in vol. 4). Note that Congress issued both Senate Reports and House Reports. Which House report is reprinted?

You have now found the current text of a statute, examined the text as it was passed into law, and looked at some of its legislative history.

The last remaining questions of this assignment require you to use the tables in the *United States Code Annotated*.

13. Use the Popular Name Table (it is in a separate volume). What is the formal name of the act commonly known as the Rate Act?

14. In real life, you will often have a session law citation or public law number and need a code citation. Usually the best way to find this is by using the tables in the code. Use the U.S.C.A. volumes labeled "Tables Volume II" and state the U.S.C.A. title and section that correspond to:

   a. 102 Stat. 3611

   b. Pub. L. No. 99-661 § 501

You have used the two annotated codes in this assignment. In law practice, you will almost never use the official code, because it is not as often updated and it does not contain the helpful features of the annotated versions. When using the annotated codes, bear in mind they each have different features and will often contain different cases. You will want to check both if you are doing an exhaustive search for annotations.

You found a session law of your code section in the *U.S. Statutes at Large*, the official publication of federal session laws. Researchers often refer to session laws when investigating the history of a law. Session laws also appear the *U.S. Code Congressional & Administrative News*, along with legislative history. You looked up the legislative history behind your code section. When seeking legislative history, you will probably check U.S.C.C.A.N. first because using it is easier than many other sources of legislative history.

Note: Federal statutory materials are available on WESTLAW and LEXIS. Some questions in this assignment can be answered online.

ASSIGNMENT TEN
FEDERAL LEGISLATIVE HISTORY
EXERCISE A

GOALS OF THIS ASSIGNMENT:
To acquaint you with the *CIS/Index* for accessing legislative documents.
To introduce you to the THOMAS website for accessing legislative documents on the Internet.

Questions 1-11 require you to use the *CIS/Index* (CIS). *CIS/Index* is also on the web known as the LexisNexis CIS Index. Your school may subscribe to this website, http://lexis-nexis.com/congcomp. **Refer to Rule 13 in *The Bluebook: A Uniform System of Citation*, 17th ed.**

CIS gives you legislative history information and abstracts of the four types of Congressional publications: reports, documents, hearings and committee prints. **Note: H.R. is the abbreviation for the House of Representatives; S. is the abbreviation for the Senate.**

1.   Assume you are seeking information on the legislative history of the act, Pub. L. No. 107-75, enacted in 2001. Start with the CIS 2001 Legislative Histories volume. You should refer to the "User Guide" before you answer these questions. Find the entry for Pub. L. No. 107-75. What is the subject or short title of the act?

2.   What is the 2001 House Report number on the bill? It is dated October 16, 2001. Cite it according to Rule 13.4 of *The Bluebook*.

3.   What is the CIS abstract number for the report from Question 2?

4.   Next, examine the CIS abstract of the May 16, 2000 House hearings on Pub. L. No. 107-75, summarized in CIS01:H781-38. On what pages in the hearing can you find James L. Martin's testimony?

5.   To obtain the full texts of the bills, reports or hearings in your library, you might have to know the Superintendent of Documents (SuDocs) number. This number begins with a "Y" and contains a colon. What is the SuDoc number of the hearing from Question 4?

Using both the 2001 CIS Index and Abstracts volumes, answer Questions 6-10.

6.   Find the Index of Subjects and Names in the Index volume. What is the CIS abstract number for the publication indexed in 2001 on postal employees?

7.   Find the abstract in the Abstracts volume. Identify your answer to Question 6 as a type of Congressional publication (i.e., report, document, hearing, committee print).

8.   Return to the Index of Subjects and Names and then go to the appropriate abstract. On what date did Ann Laundrie testify?

9.   Use the Index of Titles. What was the date of the congressional hearing titled NARAB and Beyond?

10.   Lastly, use the Index of Bill Numbers. What is the title of the December 18, 2001 report relating to Senate Bill 1379 (107th Congress)?

Now, you will search the THOMAS website. THOMAS accesses legislative information on the Internet without a fee. Go the http://thomas.loc.gov. Take a few minutes to familiarize yourself with the site.

11. Locate the **Internet Tax Nondiscrimination Act**, Pub. L. No. 107-75 by first clicking on Public Laws, then 107th Congress. Next, locate the correct public law and click on the bill number. What is the bill number that passed into law?

12. Who was the main sponsor of the bill?

13. What committee considered the bill?

14. Click on All Bill Summary and Status Information. What was the House Report Number reported by the Committee on the Judiciary on 10/16?

15. Is the full text of the report available?

16. On what date was the bill presented to the President?

ASSIGNMENT TEN
FEDERAL LEGISLATIVE HISTORY
EXERCISE B

GOALS OF THIS ASSIGNMENT:
To acquaint you with the *CIS/Index* for accessing legislative documents.
To introduce you to the THOMAS website for accessing legislative documents on the Internet.

Questions 1-11 require you to use the *CIS/Index* (CIS). *CIS/Index* is also on the web known as the LexisNexis CIS Index. Your school may subscribe to this website, http://lexis-nexis.com/congcomp. Refer to Rule 13 in *The Bluebook: A Uniform System of Citation*, 17th ed.

CIS gives you legislative history information and abstracts of the four types of Congressional publications: reports, documents, hearings and committee prints. **Note: H.R. is the abbreviation for the House of Representatives; S. is the abbreviation for the Senate.**

1. Assume you are seeking information on the legislative history of the act, Pub. L. No. 106-264, enacted in 2000. Start with the CIS 2000 Legislative Histories volume. You should refer to the "User Guide" before you answer these questions. Find the entry for Pub. L. No. 106-264. What is the subject or short title of the act?

2. What is the 2000 House Report number on H.R. 3519? Cite it according to Rule 13.4 of *The Bluebook*.

3. What is the CIS abstract number of the report from Question 2?

4. Next, examine the CIS abstract of the July 22, 1999 House hearings on Pub. L. No. 106-264, summarized in CIS00:H401-106. On what pages in the hearing can you find Jesse Jackson, Jr.'s testimony?

5.   To obtain the full texts of the bills, reports or hearings in your library, you might have to know the Superintendent of Documents (SuDocs) number. This number begins with a "Y" and contains a colon and a slash. What is the SuDoc number of the hearing from Question 4?

Using both the 2000 CIS Index and Abstracts volumes, answer Questions 6-10.

6.   Find the Index of Subjects and Names in the Index volume. What is the CIS abstract number for the publication indexed in 2000 on football?

7.   Find the Abstract in the Abstracts volume. Identify your answer to Question 6 as a type of Congressional publication (i.e., report, document, hearing, committee print).

8.   Use the Index of Subjects and Names and then go to the appropriate abstract. On what date did Clarence V. Monin testify on train and truck operator fatigue problems?

9.   Next, use the Index of Titles. What was the date of the Congressional hearings titled Obscene Material Available Via the Internet?

10. Lastly, use the Index of Bill Numbers. What is the title of the report relating to S. 302 (106th Congress)?

Now, you will search the THOMAS website. THOMAS accesses legislative information on the Internet without a fee. Go the http://thomas.loc.gov. Take a few minutes to familiarize yourself with the site.

11. Locate the **Global AIDS and Tuberculosis Relief Act of 2000**, Pub. L. No. 106-264 by first clicking on Public Laws, then 106th Congress. Next, locate the correct public law and click on the bill number. What is the bill number that passed into law?

12. Who was the main sponsor of the bill?

13. What committees considered the bill?

14. Click on All Bill Summary and Status Information. What was the House Report number reported by the House Committee on Banking and Financial Services on 3/28?

15. Is the full text of the report available?

16. On what date was the bill presented to the President?

ASSIGNMENT TEN
FEDERAL LEGISLATIVE HISTORY
EXERCISE C

GOALS OF THIS ASSIGNMENT:

To acquaint you with the *CIS/Index* for accessing legislative documents.

To introduce you to the THOMAS website for accessing legislative documents on the Internet.

Questions 1-11 require you to use the *CIS/Index* (CIS). *CIS/Index* is also on the web known as the LexisNexis CIS Index. Your school may subscribe to this website, http://lexis-nexis.com/congcomp. Refer to Rule 13 in *The Bluebook: A Uniform System of Citation*, 17th ed.

CIS gives you legislative history information and abstracts of the four types of Congressional publications: reports, documents, hearings and committee prints. **Note: H.R. is the abbreviation for the House of Representatives; S. is the abbreviation for the Senate.**

1. Assume you are seeking information on the legislative history of the act, Pub. L. No. 106-150, enacted in 1999. Using the Legislative History volume of the 1999 CIS Annual, find the entry for Pub. L. No. 106-150. You should refer to "User Guide" before you answer the questions. What is the subject or short title of the act?

2. What is the 1999 House Report number on H.R. 1665? Cite it according to Rule 13.4 of *The Bluebook*.

3. What is the CIS abstract number for the report from Question 2?

4. Next, examine the CIS abstract of the 1999 House hearings summarized in CIS99:S311-57 from May 25, 1999. On what pages in the hearing can you find Bob Carr's testimony?

5.   To obtain the full texts of the bills, reports or hearings in your library, you might have to know the Superintendent of Documents (SuDocs) number. This number begins with a "Y" and contains a colon. What is the SuDoc number of the hearing from Question 4?

Using both the 1999 CIS Index and Abstracts volumes, answer Questions 6-10.

6.   Find the Index of Subjects and Names in the Index volume. What is the CIS abstract number for the publication indexed in 1999 on eminent domain?

7.   Find the abstract in the abstracts volume. Identify your answer to Question 6 as a type of Congressional publication (i.e., report, document, hearing, committee print).

8.   Use the Index of Subjects and Names and then go to the appropriate abstract. On what date did Alan Ho testify?

9.   Use the Index of Titles. What was the date of the congressional hearing on NATO's 50th Anniversary Summit?

10.   Lastly, use the Index of Bill Numbers. What is the title of a publication relating to H.R. 22 (106th Congress)?

Now, you will search the THOMAS website. THOMAS accesses legislative information on the Internet without a fee. Go the http://thomas.loc.gov. Take a few minutes to familiarize yourself with the site.

11.   Locate the **Wilderness Battlefield Expansion**, Pub. L. No. 106-150 by first clicking on Public Law, then the106[th] Congress. Next, locate the correct public law and click on the bill number. What is the bill number that passed into law?

12.   Who was the main sponsor of the bill?

13.   What committee considered the bill?

14.   Click on All Bill Summary and Status Information. What was the House Report number reported by the House Committee on Resources on 10/4?

15.   Is the report available in full text?

16.   On what date was the bill presented to the President?

ASSIGNMENT TEN
FEDERAL LEGISLATIVE HISTORY
EXERCISE D

GOALS OF THIS ASSIGNMENT:
To acquaint you with the *CIS/Index* for accessing legislative documents.
To introduce you to the THOMAS website for accessing legislative documents on the Internet.

Questions 1-11 require you to use the *CIS/Index* Annual (CIS). *CIS/Index* is also on the web known as the LexisNexis CIS Index. Your school may subscribe to this website, http://lexis-nexis.com/congcomp. **Refer to Rule 13 in *The Bluebook: A Uniform System of Citation*, 17th ed.**

CIS gives you legislative history information and abstracts of the four types of Congressional publications: reports, documents, hearings and committee prints. **Note: H.R. is the abbreviation for the House of Representatives; S. is the abbreviation for the Senate.**

1. Assume you are seeking information on the legislative history of an act, Pub. L. No. 105-304, enacted in 1998. Start with the CIS 1998 Legislative Histories volume. You should refer to the "User Guide" before you answer these questions. Find the entry for Pub. L. No. 105-304. What is the subject or short title of the act?

2. What is the 1998 House Report number on H.R. 2281? Cite it according to Rule 13.4 of *The Bluebook.*

3. What is the CIS abstract number of the report from Question 2?

4. Next, examine the CIS abstract of the May 7, 1996 Hearings on Pub. L. No. 105-304, summarized in CIS97:S521-65. On what pages in the hearing can you find Robert L. Oakley's testimony?

5.   To obtain the full texts of the bills, reports, hearings or prints in your library, you might have to know the Superintendent of Documents (SuDocs) number. This number begins with a "Y" and contains a colon and a slash. What is the SuDoc number of this hearing in Question 4?

Using both the 1998 CIS Index and Abstracts volumes, answer Questions 6-10.

6.   Find the Index of Subjects and Names in the Index volume. What is the CIS abstract number for the publication indexed in1998 on swine?

7.   Find the abstract in the abstract volume. Identify your answer to Question 6 as a type of Congressional publication (i.e., report, document, hearing, committee print).

8.   Use the Index of Subjects and Names, and then go to the appropriate abstract. On what date did Lisa Martinez testify?

9.   Use the Index of Titles. What was the date of the Congressional hearings titled Taxpayer Subsidy of Federal Unions?

10.   Lastly, use the Index of Bill Numbers. What is the title of the Oct. 1, 1998 report relating to House Bill 563 (105th Congress)?

Now, you will search the THOMAS website. THOMAS accesses legislative information on the Internet without a fee. Go the http://thomas.loc.gov. Take a few minutes to familiarize yourself with the site.

11. Locate the **Digital Millennium Copyright Act**, Pub. L. No. 105-304 by first clicking on Public Laws, then the 105th Congress. Next, locate the correct public law and click on the bill number. What is the bill number that passed into law?

12. Who was the main sponsor of the bill?

13. What committees considered the bill?

14. Click on All Bill Summary and Status Information. What was the House Report number reported by the Committee on the Judiciary on 5/22?

15. Is the full text of part 1 of the report available?

16. On what date was the bill presented to the President?

ASSIGNMENT ELEVEN
FINDING AND CITING ADMINISTRATIVE MATERIALS
EXERCISE A

GOALS OF THIS ASSIGNMENT:
To acquaint you with finding federal regulations and administrative decisions in your library.
To familiarize you with the rules for citing regulations and administrative decisions in *The Bluebook: A Uniform System of Citation*, 17th ed.

CITATION RULES: You will need to read Rules 14.1-14.3 and Tables 1 and 13. Apply these rules as you determine the correct citation for each regulation and decision. All of the materials in this assignment are U.S. government documents and may be shelved in the government documents area of your library.

The first question requires you to find and cite a regulation in the C.F.R. Cite all federal rules and regulations to the C.F.R. by title, section, and year. Include the name of the regulation if it is commonly known by its name. **Example: 7 C.F.R. § 1902.6 (2002).**

1.   Find and cite the most recent edition of the *Code of Federal Regulations*, section 81.1 of Title 4. Do not include the name of the regulation.

The next question requires you to find and cite a regulation in the daily *Federal Register*. Citations of regulations should give the commonly used name (if appropriate), the volume and page on which the regulation begins, and the exact date. When the *Federal Register* indicates where the rule will appear in the C.F.R., give that information in parentheses. **Example: 67 Fed. Reg. 49,599 (July 31, 2002) (to be codified at 38 C.F.R. pt. 20).**

2.   Find the *Federal Register* for June 4, 2002 at p. 38,407 and cite it correctly. Do not include the name of the regulation.

Next, you must find a proposed rule (that is, one that is not promulgated) in the *Federal Register* and cite it correctly. When citing proposed rules, follow the form for final rules (see above example), but also add the exact date it was proposed. **Example: 60 Fed. Reg. 3371 (proposed Jan. 17, 1995) (to be codified at 49 C.F.R. pt. 40).**

3.   Find the *Federal Register* for January 10, 2002 at p. 1315 and cite it correctly. Do not include the name of the proposed regulation.

Now, find and cite an administrative decision or adjudication. When citing an administrative decision, cite by case name, report, and date - see Rule 14.3. The case name should only be the first-listed private party or subject-matter title. NOTE: If the case does not appear in an official agency reporter, then cite to a looseleaf service; see Rule 18 for details. **Example: *John Staurulakis, Inc.*, 4 F.C.C.R. 516 (1988).**

4.   Find the administrative decision involving CalMat Co. in volume 331 of the *Decisions and Orders of the National Labor Relations Board*. You may need to seek assistance from your librarian to locate administrative decisions in your library. Provide the full citation of the case.

The *Federal Register*, the C.F.R., and many administrative decisions are online on WESTLAW and LEXIS. You can locate administrative materials on the Internet at http://www.nara.gov and http://www.access.gpo.gov .

GOALS OF THIS ASSIGNMENT:

To acquaint you with finding federal regulations and administrative decisions in your library.

To familiarize you with the rules for citing regulations and administrative decisions in *The Bluebook: A Uniform System of Citation*, 17th ed.

CITATION RULES: You will need to read Rules 14.1-14.3 and Tables 1 and 13. Apply these rules as you determine the correct citation for each regulation and decision. All of the materials in this assignment are U.S. government documents and may be shelved in the government documents area of your library.

The first question requires you to find and cite a regulation in the C.F.R. Cite all federal rules and regulations to the C.F.R. by title, section, and year. Include the name of the regulation if it is commonly known by its name. **Example: 7 C.F.R. § 1902.6 (2002).**

1.   Find and cite the most recent edition of the *Code of Federal Regulations*, section 252.27 of Title 27. Do not include the name of the regulation.

The next question requires you to find and cite a regulation in the daily *Federal Register*. Citations of regulations should give the commonly used name (if appropriate), the volume and page on which the regulation begins, and the exact date. When the *Federal Register* indicates where the rule will appear in the C.F.R., give that information in parentheses. **Example: 67 Fed. Reg. 49,599 (July 31, 2002) (to be codified at 38 C.F.R. pt. 20).**

2.   Find the *Federal Register* for July 12, 2002 at p. 46,298 and cite it correctly. Do not include the name of the regulation.

Next, you must find a proposed rule (that is, one that is not promulgated) in the *Federal Register* and cite it correctly. When citing proposed rules, follow the form for final rules (see above example), but also add the exact date it was proposed. **Example: 60 Fed. Reg. 3371 (proposed Jan. 17, 1995) (to be codified at 49 C.F.R. pt. 40).**

3.   Find the *Federal Register* for January 25, 2002 at p. 3662 and cite it correctly. Do not include the name of the proposed regulation.

Now, find and cite an administrative decision or adjudication. When citing an administrative decision, cite by case name, report, and date - see Rule 14.3. The case name should only be the first-listed private party or subject-matter title. NOTE: If the case does not appear in an official agency reporter, then cite to a looseleaf service; see Rule 18 for details. **Example: *John Staurulakis, Inc.*, 4 F.C.C.R. 516 (1988).**

4.   Find the administrative decision involving Biltmore Broadcasting, L.L.C. in volume 17 of the *Federal Communications Commission Record*. You may need to seek assistance from your librarian to locate administrative decisions in your library. Provide the full citation of the case.

The *Federal Register*, the C.F.R., and many administrative decisions are online on WESTLAW and LEXIS. You can locate administrative materials on the Internet at http://www.nara.gov and http://www.access.gpo.gov.

GOALS OF THIS ASSIGNMENT:
To acquaint you with finding federal regulations and administrative decisions in your library.
To familiarize you with the rules for citing regulations and administrative decisions in *The Bluebook: A Uniform System of Citation*, 17th ed.

CITATION RULES: You will need to read Rules 14.1-14.3 and Tables 1 and 13. Apply these rules as you determine the correct citation for each regulation and decision. All of the materials in this assignment are U.S. government documents and may be shelved in the Government Documents area of your library.

The first question requires you to find and cite a regulation in the C.F.R. Cite all federal rules and regulations to the C.F.R. by title, section, and year. Include the name of the regulation if it is commonly known by its name. **Example: 7 C.F.R. § 1902.6 (2002).**

1.   Find and cite the most recent edition of the *Code of Federal Regulations*, section 25.21 of Title 12. Do not include the name of the regulation.

The next question requires you to find and cite a regulation in the daily *Federal Register*. Citations of regulations should give the commonly used name (if appropriate), the volume and page on which the regulation begins, and the exact date. When the *Federal Register* indicates where the rule will appear in the C.F.R., give that information in parentheses.
Example: 67 Fed. Reg. 49,599 (July 31, 2002) (to be codified at 38 C.F.R. pt. 20).

2.   Find the *Federal Register* for August 2, 2002 at p. 50,391 and cite it correctly. Do not include the name of the regulation.

Next, you must find a proposed rule (that is, one that is not promulgated) in the *Federal Register* and cite it correctly. When citing proposed rules, follow the form for final rules (see above example), but also add the exact date it was proposed. **Example: 60 Fed. Reg. 3371 (proposed Jan. 17, 1995) (to be codified at 49 C.F.R. pt. 40**).

3.   Find the *Federal Register* for March 8, 2002 at p. 10,659 and cite it correctly. Do not include the name of the proposed regulation.

Now, find and cite an administrative decision or adjudication. When citing an administrative decision, cite by case name, report, and date - see Rule 14.3. The case name should only be the first-listed private party or subject-matter title. NOTE: If the case does not appear in an official agency reporter, then cite to a looseleaf service; see Rule 18 for details. **Example: *John Staurulakis, Inc.*, 4 F.C.C.R. 516 (1988).**

4.   Find the administrative decision involving the Transfer or Operation of Lines of Railroads in Reorganization in volume 9 of the *Interstate Commerce Commission Reports*, Second Series. You may need to seek assistance from your librarian to locate administrative decisions in your library. Provide the full citation of the case.

The *Federal Register*, the C.F.R., and many administrative decisions are online on WESTLAW and LEXIS. You can locate administrative materials on the Internet at http://www.nara.gov and http://www.access.gpo.gov.

ASSIGNMENT ELEVEN
FINDING AND CITING ADMINISTRATIVE MATERIALS
EXERCISE D

GOALS OF THIS ASSIGNMENT:
To acquaint you with finding federal regulations and administrative decisions in your library.
To familiarize you with the rules for citing regulations and administrative decisions in *The Bluebook: A Uniform System of Citation*, 17thed.

CITATION RULES: You will need to read Rules 14.1-14.3 and Tables 1 and 13. Apply these rules as you determine the correct citation for each regulation and decision. All of the materials in this assignment are U.S. government documents and may be shelved in the government documents area of your library.

The first question requires you to find and cite a regulation in the C.F.R. Cite all federal rules and regulations to the C.F.R. by title, section, and year. Include the name of the regulation if it is commonly known by its name. **Example: 7 C.F.R. § 1902.6 (2002).**

1.   Find and cite the most recent edition of the *Code of Federal Regulations*, section 1308.11 of Title 21. Do not include the name of the regulation.

The next question requires you to find and cite a regulation in the daily *Federal Register*. Citations of regulations should give the commonly used name (if appropriate), the volume and page on which the regulation begins, and the exact date. When the *Federal Register* indicates where the rule will appear in the C.F.R., give that information in parentheses.
Example: 67 Fed. Reg. 49,599 (July 31, 2002) (to be codified at 38 C.F.R. pt. 20).

2.   Find the *Federal Register* for August 19, 2002 at p. 53,767 and cite it correctly. Do not include the name of the regulation.

Next, you must find a proposed rule (that is, one that is not promulgated) in the *Federal Register* and cite it correctly. When citing proposed rules, follow the form for final rules (see above example), but also add the exact date it was proposed. **Example: 60 Fed. Reg. 3371 (proposed Jan. 17, 1995) (to be codified at 49 C.F.R. pt. 40).**

3. Find the *Federal Register* for April 1, 2002 at p. 15,344 and cite it correctly. Do not include the name of the proposed regulation.

Now, find and cite an administrative decision or adjudication. When citing an administrative decision, cite by case name, report, and date - see Rule 14.3. The case name should only be the first-listed private party or subject-matter title. NOTE: If the case does not appear in an official agency reporter, then cite to a looseleaf service; see Rule 18 for details. **Example: *John Staurulakis, Inc.*, 4 F.C.C.R. 516 (1988).**

4. Find the administrative decision involving Life Fitness in volume 124 of the *Federal Trade Commission Decisions*. You may need to seek assistance from your librarian to locate administrative decisions in your library. Assume that the subsequent history of the case is unknown. Provide the full citation of the case.

The *Federal Register*, the C.F.R., and many administrative decisions are online on WESTLAW and LEXIS. You can locate administrative materials on the Internet at http://www.nara.gov and http://www.access.gpo.gov.

ASSIGNMENT TWELVE
FEDERAL ADMINISTRATIVE RULES AND REGULATIONS
EXERCISE A

GOALS OF THIS ASSIGNMENT:
To develop your ability to find printed federal final and proposed regulations on a specific topic, issued by a specific agency, or issued pursuant to authority granted by a particular statute.
To give you experience in determining whether an agency has modified or eliminated a regulation.

> To answer Questions 1-2, use the Index volume to the *Code of Federal Regulations* (any year), published by the Government Printing Office.
> Note: The C.F.R. and *Federal Register* are also located on LEXIS, WESTLAW, and on the Internet at: http://www.access.gpo.gov/nara/cfr.

1. Using the appropriate table, labeled "Authorities," in the Index volume, state which title and part of the C.F.R. were promulgated under the authority of 49 U.S.C. § 44715, a related code section to the one you used in Assignment Nine. By using this table you can find regulations if you already have the U.S.C. citation. Cite to the **first** C.F.R. citation, if there is more than one citation.

2. Now use the subject index in the same Index volume. Find and cite the regulations on special milk programs for children.

    Reshelve the Index volume.

3. Find the text of the regulation part from the previous question. What is the statutory authority for the regulation part? State the **first** reference to the U.S.C. as printed in the C.F.R.

4. Where did the first regulation (§ 215.1) from the part in Question 3 appear in the *Federal Register*? State the source note as printed in the C.F.R.

Assume that you want to update a regulation to learn if it has been amended, repealed or superseded. Follow these steps:

1) Examine the regulation in the most current C.F.R. volume. Note the date of revision on the front cover.

2) Consult the monthly *List of C.F.R. Sections Affected* (*LSA*) pamphlet to see if they list your section. If there has been a change, there will be a source note to page numbers in the *Federal Register*. You will need to cover the time period from step (1) to the most recent *LSA* pamphlet. Note that the December, March, June and September issues cumulate changes for particular titles, so you should only have to check a few pamphlets.

3) Consult the last issue of the month of the *Federal Register* for each complete month since the month on the cover of the *LSA* pamphlet. Check the CFR PARTS AFFECTED DURING [month] table near the back of the issue. Do not make the mistake of consulting the CFR PARTS AFFECTED IN THIS ISSUE table near the front of each *Federal Register* issue.

4) Finally, consult the most recent issue of the *Federal Register* available and check the CFR PARTS AFFECTED DURING [month] table near the back. This table cumulates through the month. Note the date of issue.

Although this process is complicated, you should follow it each time you use a federal regulation (either in print or, effortlessly, on WESTLAW, LEXIS or the Internet).

Now use the *List of C.F.R. Sections Affected* to answer Questions 5 and 6.

5. Using the *List of CFR Sections Affected*, June 2002, determine if any change occurred in 36 C.F.R. § 242.22. What is the status of that section?

6. Where would you find this change in the 2002 *Federal Register*?

ASSIGNMENT TWELVE
FEDERAL ADMINISTRATIVE RULES AND REGULATIONS
EXERCISE B

GOALS OF THIS ASSIGNMENT:
To develop your ability to find printed federal final and proposed regulations on a specific topic, issued by a specific agency, or issued pursuant to authority granted by a particular statute.
To give you experience in determining whether an agency has modified or eliminated a regulation.

To answer Questions 1-2, use the Index volume to the *Code of Federal Regulations* (any year), published by the Government Printing Office.
Note: The C.F.R. and *Federal Register* are also located on LEXIS, WESTLAW, and on the Internet at: http://www.access.gpo.gov/nara/cfr.

1. Using the appropriate table, labeled "Authorities," in the Index volume, state which title and part of the C.F.R. were promulgated under the authority of 42 U.S.C. § 4821, a related code section to the one you used in Assignment Nine. By using this table you can find regulations if you already have the U.S.C. citation. Cite to the **first** C.F.R. citation, if there is more than one citation.

2. Now use the subject index in the same Index volume. Find and cite the regulations on full size baby cribs.

    Reshelve the Index volume.

3. Find the text of the regulation part from the previous question. What is the statutory authority for the regulation part? State the **first** source note to the U.S.C. as printed in the C.F.R.

4. Where did the first regulation (§ 1508.1) from the part in Question 3 appear in the *Federal Register*? State the source note as printed in the C.F.R.

Assume that you want to update a regulation to learn if it has been amended, repealed or superseded. Follow these steps:

1) Examine the regulation in the most current C.F.R. volume. Note the date of revision on the front cover.

2) Consult the monthly *List of C.F.R. Sections Affected* (*LSA*) pamphlet to see if they list your section. If there has been a change, there will be a source note to page numbers in the *Federal Register*. You will need to cover the time period from step (1) to the most recent *LSA* pamphlet. Note that the December, March, June and September issues cumulate changes for particular titles, so you should only have to check a few pamphlets.

3) Consult the last issue of the month of the *Federal Register* for each complete month since the month on the cover of the *LSA* pamphlet. Check the CFR PARTS AFFECTED DURING [month] table near the back of the issue. Do not make the mistake of consulting the CFR PARTS AFFECTED IN THIS ISSUE table near the front of each *Federal Register* issue.

4) Finally, consult the most recent issue of the *Federal Register* available and check the CFR PARTS AFFECTED DURING [month]. This table cumulates through the month. Note the date of issue.

Although this process is complicated, you should follow it each time you use a federal regulation (either in print or, effortlessly, on WESTLAW, LEXIS or the Internet).

Now use the *List of C.F.R. Sections Affected* to answer Questions 5 and 6.

5. Using the *List of CFR Sections Affected*, December 2002, determine if any change occurred in 7 C.F.R. § 1410.2. What is the status of that section?

6. Where would you find this change in the 2002 *Federal Register*?

ASSIGNMENT TWELVE
FEDERAL ADMINISTRATIVE RULES AND REGULATIONS
EXERCISE C

GOALS OF THIS ASSIGNMENT:

To develop your ability to find printed federal final and proposed regulations on a specific topic, issued by a specific agency, or issued pursuant to authority granted by a particular statute.

To give you experience in determining whether an agency has modified or eliminated a regulation.

To answer Questions 1-2, use the Index volume to the *Code of Federal Regulations* (any year), published by the Government Printing Office.
Note: The C.F.R. and *Federal Register* are also located on LEXIS, WESTLAW, and on the Internet at: http://www.access.gpo.gov/nara/cfr.

1. Using the appropriate table, labeled "Authorities," in the Index volume, state which title and part of the C.F.R. were promulgated under the authority of 42 U.S.C. § 6103, a related code section to the one you used in Assignment Nine. By using this table you can find regulations if you already have the U.S.C. citation. Cite to the **first** C.F.R. citation, if there is more than one citation.

2. Now use the subject index in the same Index volume. Find and cite the regulations on exporting plums.

    Reshelve the Index volume.

3. Find the text of the regulation part from the previous question. What is the statutory authority for the regulation part? State the **first** reference to the U.S.C. as printed in the C.F.R.

4. Where did the first regulation (§ 35.1) from the part in Question 3 appear in the *Federal Register*? State the source note as printed in the C.F.R.

Assume that you want to update a regulation to learn if it has been amended, repealed, or superseded. Follow these steps:

1) Examine the regulation in the most current C.F.R. volume. Note the date of revision on the front cover.

2) Consult the monthly *List of C.F.R. Sections Affected (LSA)* pamphlet to see if they list your section. If there has been a change, there will be a source note to page numbers in the *Federal Register*. You will need to cover the time period from step (1) to the most recent *LSA* pamphlet. Note that the December, March, June and September issues cumulate changes for particular titles, so you should only have to check a few pamphlets.

3) Consult the last issue of the month of the *Federal Register* for each complete month since the month on the cover of the *LSA* pamphlet. Check the CFR PARTS AFFECTED DURING [month] table near the back of the issue. Do not make the mistake of consulting the CFR PARTS AFFECTED IN THIS ISSUE table near the front of each *Federal Register* issue.

4) Finally, consult the most recent issue of the *Federal Register* available and check the CFR PARTS AFFECTED DURING [month]. This table cumulates through the month. Note the date of issue.

Although this process is complicated, you should follow it each time you use a federal regulation (either in print or, effortlessly, or on WESTLAW, LEXIS or the Internet).

Now use the *List of C.F.R. Sections Affected* to answer Questions 5 and 6.

5. Using the *List of CFR Sections Affected*, September 2002, determine if any change occurred in 42 C.F.R. § 457.10. What is the status of that section?

6. Where would you find this change in the 2002 *Federal Register*?

GOALS OF THIS ASSIGNMENT:

To develop your ability to find printed federal final and proposed regulations on a specific topic, issued by a specific agency, or issued pursuant to authority granted by a particular statute.

To give you experience in determining whether an agency has modified or eliminated a regulation.

To answer Questions 1-2, use the Index volume to the *Code of Federal Regulations* (any year), published by the Government Printing Office.
Note: The C.F.R. and *Federal Register* are also located on LEXIS, WESTLAW, and on the Internet at: http://www.access.gpo.gov/nara/cfr.

1. Using the appropriate table, labeled "Authorities," in the Index volume, state which title and parts of the C.F.R. were promulgated under the authority of 17 U.S.C. § 1007, the code section you used in Assignment Nine. By using this table you can find regulations if you already have the U.S.C. citation. Cite to the **first** C.F.R. citation, if there is more than one citation.

2. Now use the subject index in the same Index volume. Find and cite the regulations on apricots grown in Washington.

    Reshelve the Index volume.

3. Find the text of the regulation part from the previous question. What is the statutory authority for the regulation part? State the **first** source note to the U.S.C. as printed in the C.F.R.

4. Where did the first regulation (§ 922.1) from the part in Question 3 appear in the *Federal Register*? State the source note as printed in the C.F.R.

Assume that you want to update a regulation to learn if it has been amended, repealed or superseded. Follow these steps:

1) Examine the regulation in the most current C.F.R. volume. Note the date of revision on the front cover.

2) Consult the monthly *List of C.F.R. Sections Affected (LSA)* pamphlet to see if they list your section. If there has been a change, there will be a source note to page numbers in the *Federal Register*. You will need to cover the time period from step (1) to the most recent *LSA* pamphlet. Note that the December, March, June and September issues cumulate changes for particular titles, so you should only have to check a few pamphlets.

3) Consult the last issue of the month of the *Federal Register* for each complete month since the month on the cover of the *LSA* pamphlet. Check the CFR PARTS AFFECTED DURING [month] table near the back of the issue. Do not make the mistake of consulting the CFR PARTS AFFECTED IN THIS ISSUE table near the front of each *Federal Register* issue.

4) Finally, consult the most recent issue of the *Federal Register* available and check the CFR PARTS AFFECTED DURING [month]. This table cumulates through the month. Note the date of issue.

Although this process is complicated, you should follow it each time you use a federal regulation (either in print or, effortlessly, on WESTLAW or LEXIS).

Now use the *List of C.F.R. Sections Affected* to answer Questions 5 and 6.

5. Using the *List of CFR Sections Affected*, March 2002, determine if any change occurred in 26 C.F.R. § 301.7611-1. What is the status of that section?

6. Where would you find this change in the 2002 *Federal Register*?

ASSIGNMENT THIRTEEN
REVIEW--FINDING STATUTES AND REGULATIONS
EXERCISE A

GOAL OF THIS ASSIGNMENT:
To require you to perform several steps in statutory and regulatory research problems.

In this assignment, you will review statutory and regulatory research. You will find statutory law, legislative history, regulations and library references. The starting point for your research is the **Long-Term Care Security Act.** Use U.S.C.A. for Questions 1-5.

1.   Use the Popular Name Table in the U.S.C.A. and state the code citation for the **Long-Term Care Security Act**.

Look up the act in U.S.C.A. and answer Questions 2-5.

2.   Examine **§ 9003.** What is the Public Law number of the 2000 act?

3.   Under "Library References," what are the West topic and key numbers on federal courts ?

4.   Now examine the encyclopedia references listed under **§ 9003**. State the sections in C.J.S. for the topic *United States*.

5.   Next use U.S.C.A. to find the legislative history of the 2000 act in U.S.C.C.A.N. Obtain the citation to U.S.C.C.A.N. in the **Historical and Statutory Notes** to 5 U.S.C.A. § 9003. On what page of the 2000 U.S.C.C.A.N. does the legislative history begin?

Reshelve U.S.C.A. and find U.S.C.C.A.N.

6. Examine the legislative history in the 2000 U.S.C.C.A.N. from Question 5. Which House report is reprinted?

Reshelve U.S.C.C.A.N. and locate the U.S.C.A. and C.F.R.

7. Assume that your task is to find regulations listed under 47 U.S.C.A. § 202. List the administrative law citations on radio broadcast services as they appear in the U.S.C.A.

8. Look up the first listed regulation from Question 7 in the C.F.R. List the volume and page number where the regulation originally appeared in the 1982 issue of the *Federal Register*.

This assignment will not require you to update the regulations. To do so you would need to consult the *List of C.F.R. Sections Affected* (LSA) and the *Federal Register*.

ASSIGNMENT THIRTEEN
REVIEW--FINDING STATUTES AND REGULATIONS
EXERCISE B

GOAL OF THIS ASSIGNMENT:
To require you to perform several steps in statutory and regulatory research problems.

In this assignment, you will review statutory and regulatory research. You will find statutory law, legislative history, regulations and library references. The starting point for your research is the **Lower Saint Croix River Act of 1972.** Use U.S.C.A. for Questions 1-5.

1. Use the Popular Name Table in the U.S.C.A. and state the code citation for the **Lower Saint Croix River Act of 1972.**

   Look up the act in U.S.C.A. and answer Questions 2-5.

2. Examine **§ 1274**. What is the Public Law number of the October 25, 1972 act? NOTE: Look in parentheses at the end of the text of the act.

3. Find the "Library References" for **§ 1274** and list the C.J.S. sections for the topic *Waters*.

4. Examine the case annotations for **§ 1274**. State the name of the 1998 Northern District of California federal case listed under "Injunctions."

5. Next use U.S.C.A. to find the legislative history of the 1972 act in U.S.C.C.A.N. Obtain the citation to U.S.C.C.A.N. in the **Historical and Statutory Notes** to 16 U.S.C.A. § 1274. On what page of the 1972 U.S.C.C.A.N. does the legislative history begin?

Reshelve U.S.C.A. and find U.S.C.C.A.N.

6. Examine the legislative history in 1972 U.S.C.C.A.N. from Question 5. Which House report was reprinted?

Reshelve U.S.C.C.A.N. and locate the U.S.C.A. and C.F.R.

7. Assume that your task is to find regulations listed under **7 U.S.C.A. § 923**. List the administrative law citations on nondiscrimination requirements as they appear in the U.S.C.A.

8. Look up the first listed regulation from Question 7 in the C.F.R. List the volume and page number where the regulation originally appeared in the1964 *Federal Register*.

This assignment will not require you to update the regulations. To do so you would need to consult the *List of C.F.R. Sections Affected* (LSA) and the *Federal Register*.

ASSIGNMENT THIRTEEN
REVIEW--FINDING STATUTES AND REGULATIONS
EXERCISE C

GOAL OF THIS ASSIGNMENT:

To require you to perform several steps in statutory and regulatory research problems.

In this assignment, you will review statutory and regulatory research. You will find statutory law, legislative history, regulations and library references. The starting point for your research is the **National Skill Standards Act of 1994.** Use U.S.C.A. for Questions 1-5.

1. Use the Popular Name Table in the U.S.C.A. and state the code citation for the **National Skill Standards Act of 1994** enacted March 31, 1994.

    Look up the act in U.S.C.A. and answer Questions 2-5.

2. Examine **§ 5933.** What is the Public Law number of the March 31, 1994 act?

3. Find the "Library References" for **§ 5933** and list the C.J.S. sections for the topic *United States.*

4. Under "Library References," what are the West topic and key numbers on United States?

5. Next use U.S.C.A. to find the legislative history of the 1994 act in U.S.C.C.A.N. Obtain the citation to U.S.C.C.A.N. in the **Historical and Statutory Notes** to 20 U.S.C.A. § 5933. On what page of the 1994 U.S.C.C.A.N. does the legislative history begin?

Reshelve U.S.C.A. and find U.S.C.C.A.N.

6.   Examine the legislative history in U.S.C.C.A.N. from Question 5. Which reports are reprinted?

Reshelve U.S.C.C.A.N. and locate the U.S.C.A. and the C.F.R.

7.   Assume that your task is to find regulations listed under **22 U.S.C.A. § 2506**. List the administrative law citations on career and career - conditional employment as they appear in the U.S.C.A.

8.   Look up the first listed regulation from Question 7 in C.F.R. List the volume and page number where the regulation originally appeared in the 1968 *Federal Register*.

This assignment will not require you to update the regulations. To do so you would need to consult the *List of C.F.R. Sections Affected* (LSA) and the *Federal Register*.

ASSIGNMENT THIRTEEN
REVIEW--FINDING STATUTES AND REGULATIONS
EXERCISE D

GOAL OF THIS ASSIGNMENT:
To require you to perform several steps in statutory and regulatory research problems.

In this assignment, you will review statutory and regulatory research. You will find statutory law, legislative history, regulations and library references. The starting point for your research is the **Mobile Telecommunications Sourcing Act.** Use U.S.C.A. for Questions 1-5.

1. Use the Popular Name Table in the U.S.C.A. and state the code citation for the 2000 **Mobile Telecommunications Sourcing Act.**

   Look up the act in U.S.C.A. and answer Questions 2-5.

2. Examine **§ 116**. What is the Public Law number of the 2000 act?

3. Find the "Library References" for **§ 116** and list the C.J.S. sections of the topic *Telegraphs, Telephones, Radio and Television.*

4. Under "Library References," what are the West topic and key numbers on Telecommunications?

5. Next use U.S.C.A. to find the legislative history of the 2000 act in U.S.C.C.A.N. Obtain the citation to U.S.C.C.A.N. in the **Historical and Statutory Notes** to 4 U.S.C.A. § 116. On what page of the 2000 U.S.C.C.A.N. does the legislative history begin?

Reshelve U.S.C.A. and find U.S.C.C.A.N.

6. Examine the legislative history from Question 5. Which report is reprinted?

Reshelve U.S.C.C.A.N. and locate the U.S.C.A. and the C.F.R.

7. Assume that your task is to find regulations listed under **15 U.S.C.A. § 79a**. List the administrative law citations on General Rules as they appear in the U.S.C.A.

8. Look up the first regulation from Question 7 in the C.F.R. List the volume and page number where the regulation originally appeared in the 1941 *Federal Register*.

This assignment will not require you to update the regulations. To do so you would need to consult the *List of C.F.R. Sections Affected* (LSA) and the *Federal Register*.

ASSIGNMENT FOURTEEN
SECONDARY AUTHORITY
EXERCISE A

GOALS OF THIS ASSIGNMENT:

To familiarize you with one of the two major legal encyclopedias and your state legal encyclopedia.

To introduce you to the legal periodical indexes and how to cite legal periodical articles.

To show you how to find treatises in your library.

Answer Questions 1-2 using *American Jurisprudence 2d.*

1.   Provide the complete citation to the section that discusses guaranteeing specific results from plastic surgery. Use *Bluebook* form, Rule 15.7(a).

2.   Look up the section. State the name of the Massachusetts case that Am. Jur. 2d cites that discusses an action for breach of contract.

3.   Does your state have a legal encyclopedia? If so, state the title of the encyclopedia.

To answer Question 4, use the *Index to Legal Periodicals*. Question 5 relates to the answer in Question 4.

4.   Provide the citation to a 1955 article on the enforceability of a religious antenuptial agreement under Jewish law. Use Rule 16 and Table 14. Look at the actual article to cite it.

5.   If your law library holds this issue, where is the law review located in your library? Provide either a row number or call number. Indicate if your library has the article online.

To answer Questions 6 and 7, use either *LegalTrac* or the *Current Law Index*. *Current Law Index* has both a Subject Index and an Author/Title and Supplementary Indexes. Refer to Rule 16 and Table 14. Look at the actual articles to cite them.

6. Provide the complete citation to a 1985 article on the putative marriage doctrine.

7. State the citation of the 2001 article on the case *Shaw v. Murphy* that appeared in the ABA Journal. Note: This magazine is not consecutively paged, so follow Rule 16.4.

You should use your library's online catalog to answer questions 8 and 9.

8. Find the 2001 hornbook on the law of agency and partnership by William A. Gregory in your library. Cite it according to Rule 15.

9. Locate the 2003 nutshell on juvenile justice administration by Barry C. Feld. Provide the call number or location of the book in your library.

ASSIGNMENT FOURTEEN
SECONDARY AUTHORITY
EXERCISE B

GOALS OF THIS ASSIGNMENT:
To familiarize you with the use one of the two major legal encyclopedias and your state legal encyclopedia.
To introduce you to the legal periodical indexes and how to cite legal periodical articles.
To show you how to find treatises in your library.

Answer Questions 1 and 2 using *American Jurisprudence 2d.*

1.   Provide the complete citation of the section which discusses if a walking cane would be considered a deadly weapon in a robbery. Use *Bluebook* form, Rule 15.7(a).

2.   Look up the section. State the name of the New York case that Am. Jur. 2d cites under the discussion of a conviction of attempted first-degree robbery with a dangerous weapon using a broomstick-type of bat.

3.   Does your state have a legal encyclopedia? If so, state the title of the encyclopedia.

To answer Question 4, use the *Index to Legal Periodicals*. Question 5 relates to the answer in Question 4.

4.   Provide the complete citation to a 1979 article on propaganda.

5.   If your law library holds this issue, where is the law review located in your library? Provide either a row number or call number. Indicate if your library has the article online.

To answer Questions 6 and 7 use either *LegalTrac* or the *Current Law Index*. *Current Law Index* has both a Subject Index and an Author/Title and Supplementary Indexes. Refer to Rule 16 and Table 14. Look at the actual articles to cite them.

6.   Provide the citation to the 1984 article on tax issues arising on fruit orchards.

7.   State the citation of the 2000 article on the case *Florida v. J.L.* that appeared in the ABA Journal. Note: This journal is not consecutively paged, so follow Rule 16.4.

You should use your library's online catalog to answer questions 8 and 9.

8.   Find the 2000 hornbook on health law by Barry R. Furrow. Cite it according to Rule 15.

9.   Find the 2001 nutshell on admiralty by Frank L. Maraist. Provide the call number or location of the book in your library.

ASSIGNMENT FOURTEEN
SECONDARY AUTHORITY
EXERCISE C

GOALS OF THIS ASSIGNMENT:
To familiarize you with one of the two major legal encyclopedias and your state legal encyclopedia.
To introduce you to the legal periodical indexes and how to cite legal periodical articles.
To show you how to find treatises in your library.

Answer Questions 1 and 2 using *American Jurisprudence 2d.*

1.   Provide the complete citation of the sections that discuss lawn mowers as dangerous instrumentalities. Use *Bluebook* form, Rule 15.7(a).

2.   Look up the sections. State the name of an Alabama case that Am. Jur. 2d cites under the discussion that lawn mowers have been held not to be inherently dangerous instrumentalities.

3.   Does your state have a legal encyclopedia? If so, state the title of the encyclopedia.

To answer Question 4, use the *Index to Legal Periodicals*. Question 5 relates to the answer in Question 4.

4.   Provide the correct citation to a 1970 article on the admissibility of death reports. Use Rule 16 and Table 14. Look at the actual article to cite it.

5.   If your law library holds this issue, where is the law review located in your library? Provide either a row number or call number. Indicate if your library has the article online.

> **To answer Questions 6 and 7, use either *LegalTrac* or the *Current Law Index*.** *Current Law Index* has both a Subject Index and an Author/Title and Supplementary Indexes. Refer to Rule 16 and Table 14. Look at the actual articles to cite them.

6. Provide the citation to a 1993 article on incompetency in guardianship.

7. State the citation of the 1998 article written about the case *Jackson v. Bennion* that appeared in the ABA Journal. Note: This journal is not consecutively paged, so follow Rule 16.4.

> **You should use your library's online catalog to answer questions 8 and 9.**

8. Find the 2001 hornbook on local government law by Osborne M. Reynolds, Jr. Cite according to Rule 15.

9. Find the 2001 nutshell on children and the law by Sarah H. Ramsey. Provide the call number or location in your library.

ASSIGNMENT FOURTEEN
SECONDARY AUTHORITY
EXERCISE D

GOALS OF THIS ASSIGNMENT:
To familiarize you with one of the two major legal encyclopedias and your state legal encyclopedia.
To introduce you to the legal periodical indexes and how to cite legal periodical articles.
To show you how to find treatises in your library.

Answer Questions 1 and 2 using *American Jurisprudence 2d.*

1. Provide the complete citation to the section that discusses that promotion from one college class to another is within the discretion of the faculty. Use *Bluebook* form, Rule 15.7(a).

2. Look up the section. State the name of the Florida case that Am. Jur. 2d cites that addresses the topic from Question 1.

3. Does your state have a legal encyclopedia? If so, state the title of the encyclopedia.

To answer Question 4, use the *Index to Legal Periodicals*. Question 5 relates to the answer in Question 4.

4. Provide the correct citation to a 1964 article on federal preemption and state conservation in natural resources. Use Rule 16 and Table 14. Look at the actual article to cite to it.

5. If your law library holds this issue, where is the law review located in your library? Provide either a row number or call number. Indicate if your library has the article online.

To answer Questions 6 and 7, use either *LegalTrac* or the *Current Law Index*. *Current Law Index* has both a Subject Index and an Author/Title and Supplementary Indexes. Refer to Rule 16 and Table 14. Look at the actual articles to cite them.

6. Provide the complete citation to a 1999 article on utilizing trees in New York City.

7. State the citation of the 2001 article written about the case *Kyllo v. United States* that appeared in the ABA Journal. Note: This journal is not consecutively paged, so follow Rule 16.4.

You should use your library's online catalog to answer questions 8 and 9.

8. Find the 2001 hornbook on corporate income taxation by Douglas A. Kahn and Jeffrey S. Lehman in your library. Cite it according to Rule 15.

9. Find the 1995 nutshell on family law by Harry D. Krause. Provide the call number or location in your library.

ASSIGNMENT FIFTEEN
REVIEW--FINDING SECONDARY AUTHORITY
EXERCISE A

GOALS OF THIS ASSIGNMENT:
To review the use of sources of secondary authority.
To emphasize how the various publications cross reference users to other materials.

In this review you will practice using secondary authority. Of necessity, this exercise is more "open"; there may be several right answers to some questions. In this assignment you will use hornbooks, nutshells, legal periodical indexes, and the *American Law Reports* (A.L.R.).

1. The topic you will be researching is the factor of race in adoption placements. At this point, write down the relevant key words and synonyms that you could possibly use to search this topic in different indexes.

2. Into what broad areas of the law does this question fall?

3. Find the current hornbook in this subject area (it is probably on reserve). State the complete citation of the latest edition. Use Rule 15 of *The Bluebook*.

4. Is there any discussion of the topic in the hornbook from Question 3? If so, list the page number.

5. Find a current nutshell that discusses the topic. State the title of the nutshell.

6. Try the periodical indexes. Find a 1997 article on interracial adoptions, specifically the Adoption Antidiscrimination Act of 1995 that appeared in the *John Marshall Law Review*. Locate the article in your library and cite it according to Rule 16 of *The Bluebook*.

Reshelve periodical indexes and periodical and use A.L.R. to answer Questions 7-9.

7. Another source of secondary authority is A.L.R. Use the A.L.R. Index and find an A.L.R.4th annotation published in 1984 on the problem from Question 1. Provide the citation according to Rule 16.6.5.

8. Now examine the beginning of the annotation. Note the different types of cross references to other publications and to related annotations. If you next wanted to find some discussion of this issue in a legal encyclopedia, cite the source listed.

9. Before you read any further, check the pocket part of the annotation. Has this annotation been superseded or supplemented?

You have just finished research similar to that for an "open" memo in law school. Of course, in actual research, you would read and update the actual cases, whereas in this assignment you stopped at the secondary authority.

ASSIGNMENT FIFTEEN
REVIEW--FINDING SECONDARY AUTHORITY
EXERCISE B

GOALS OF THIS ASSIGNMENT:
To review the use of sources of secondary authority.
To emphasize how the various publications cross reference users to other materials.

In this review you will practice using secondary authority. Of necessity, this exercise is more "open"; there may be several right answers to some questions. In this assignment you will use hornbooks, nutshells, legal periodical indexes, and the *America Law Reports* (A.L.R.).

1. The topic you will be researching is the validity of statutes requiring return deposits on drink containers to control waste pollution. At this point, write down the relevant key words and synonyms that you could possibly use to search this topic in different indexes.

2. Into what broad area of the law does this question fall?

3. Find a current hornbook in this subject area (it is probably on reserve). State the complete citation of the latest edition. Use Rule 15 of *The Bluebook*.

4. Is there any discussion of your specific issue in the hornbook from Question 3? If so, list the page number.

5. Find a current nutshell on the topic. State the title of the nutshell.

6. Try the periodical indexes. Find a 1985 article on Oregon's recycling act that appeared in the journal, *Environmental Law*. Locate the article in your library and cite it according to Rule 16 in *The Bluebook*.

    Reshelve periodical indexes and periodical and use A.L.R. to answer Questions 7-9.

7. Another source of secondary authority is A.L.R. Use the A.L.R. Index and find an A.L.R.3d annotation published in 1976 on the problem from Question 1. Provide the citation according to Rule 16.6.5.

8. Now examine the beginning of the annotation. Note the different types of cross references to other publications and to related annotations. If you next wanted to find some discussion of this issue in a legal encyclopedia, cite the **first** source listed.

9. Before you read any further, check the pocket part of the annotation. Has this annotation been superseded or supplemented?

    You have just finished research similar to that for an "open" memo in law school. Of course, in actual research, you would read and update the actual cases, whereas in this assignment you stopped at the secondary authority.

ASSIGNMENT FIFTEEN
REVIEW--FINDING SECONDARY AUTHORITY
EXERCISE C

GOALS OF THIS ASSIGNMENT:
To review the use of sources of secondary authority.
To emphasize how the various publications cross reference users to other materials.

In this review you will practice using secondary authority. Of necessity, this exercise is more "open"; there may be several right answers to some questions. In this assignment you will use hornbooks, nutshells, legal periodical indexes, and the *American Law Reports*.

1. The topic you will be researching is the right of accused in criminal prosecution to retain counsel during mental or physical examinations. At this point, write down the relevant key words and synonyms that you could possibly use to search this topic in different indexes.

2. Into what broad area of the law does this question fall?

3. Find a current hornbook in this subject area (it is probably on reserve). State the complete citation of the latest edition. Use Rule 15 of *The Bluebook*.

4. Is there any discussion of your specific issue in the hornbook from Question 3? If so, list the page or section number.

5. Find a current nutshell on the topic. State the title of the nutshell.

6. Try the periodical indexes. Find a 1980 article on the right to counsel during psychiatric examinations of criminal defendants published in the *Villanova Law Review*. Locate the article in your library and cite it according to Rule 16 in *The Bluebook*.

    Reshelve periodical indexes and periodical and use A.L.R. to answer Questions 7-9.

7. Another source of secondary authority is A.L.R. Use the A.L.R. Index and find an A.L.R.4th annotation published in 1981 on the problem from Question 1, specifically, that the accused is entitled to counsel at a psychiatric exam on the ground that the exam constitutes a "critical stage" of the procedure. Provide the full citation according to Rule 16.6.5.

8. Now examine the beginning of the annotation. Note the different types of cross references to other publications and to related annotations. If you next wanted to find some discussion of this issue in a legal encyclopedia, cite the source listed.

9. Before you read any further, check the pocket part of the annotation. Has this annotation been superseded or supplemented?

    You have just finished research similar to that for an "open" memo in law school. Of course, in actual research, you would read and update the actual cases, whereas in this assignment you stopped at the secondary authority.

ASSIGNMENT FIFTEEN
REVIEW--FINDING SECONDARY AUTHORITY
EXERCISE D

GOALS OF THIS ASSIGNMENT:
To review the use of sources of secondary authority.
To emphasize how the various publications cross reference users to other materials.

In this review you will practice using secondary authority. Of necessity, this exercise is more "open"; there may be several right answers to some questions. In this assignment you will use hornbooks, nutshells, legal periodical indexes, and the *American Law Reports* (A.L.R.).

1. The topic you will be researching is what constitutes religious harassment in employment situations. At this point, write down the relevant key words and synonyms that you could possibly use to search this topic in different indexes.

2. Into what broad area of the law does this question fall?

3. Find a current hornbook or treatise in this subject area (it is probably on reserve). State the complete citation of the latest edition. Use Rule 15 of *The Bluebook*.

4. Is there any discussion of your specific issue in the hornbook or treatise from Question 3? If so, list the page or section numbers.

5. Find a current nutshell that discusses this topic. State the title of the nutshell.

6.   Try the periodical indexes. Find a 2000 article on when religious expression creates a hostile work environment that appeared in the *New York University Journal of Legislation and Public Policy.* Locate the article in your library and cite it according to Rule 16 in *The Bluebook*.

Reshelve periodical indexes and periodical and use A.L.R. to answer Questions 7-9.

7.   Another source of secondary authority is A.L.R. Use the A.L.R. Index and find an A.L.R. Fed. annotation published in 1998 on the problem from Question 1. Provide the citation according to Rule 16.6.5.

8.   Now examine the beginning of the annotation. Note the different types of cross references to other publications and to related annotations. If you next wanted to find some discussion of this issue in a legal encyclopedia, cite the source listed.

9.   Before you read any further, check the pocket part of the annotation. Has this annotation been superseded or supplemented?

You have just finished research similar to that for an "open" memo in law school. Of course, in actual research, you would read and update the actual sources, whereas in this assignment you stopped at the secondary authority.

ASSIGNMENT SIXTEEN
WESTLAW – PART ONE

GOALS OF THIS ASSIGNMENT:
To formulate effective search strategies in researching case law.
To introduce you to terms and connectors searching, natural language searching, field searching, FIND, KeyCite, and Table of Authorities.

Use **WESTLAW** on the Internet at http://lawschool.westlaw.com. Refer to Rule 18.1 on Commercial Electronic Databases in *The Bluebook*.

Answer Question1 before you sign on WESTLAW.

1.   Assume you want to find state cases on the following fact situation. You are an attorney representing a baseball coach who was assaulted by a volunteer manager and assistant coaches of the opposing team. He wants to know if the league is responsible for his injuries. Formulate your query by choosing terms and connectors to specify the relationship between the terms. Use the WESTLAW materials. Write your query using terms and connectors.

2.   **Sign on WESTLAW to complete the assignment**. You want to find an Illinois state case that deals with this fact situation. Use the **Directory** link at the top of the page. You can use the Database Wizard or browse the Directory. What is the appropriate database identifier for this research?

3.   Retrieve a 2000 Supreme Court of Illinois opinion concerning the query from Question 1. What is the complete citation of the case?

4.   Natural Language searching on WESTLAW allows you to search using standard English instead of terms and connectors. To change to Natural Language, select the **Edit Search** link. Now click on **Natural Language**. Use the same fact situation from Question 1 and type your search. Did you find the same Supreme Court of Illinois case from 2000?

KeyCite is West's citation service that enables you to determine if your case is good law and to find other sources that have cited your case. When viewing a particular case, you will see a "KC History" tab and a "KC Citing Ref" tab. You may also see case history indicators in the document header. If the case has negative history, you will see either a red or yellow case status flag. If the case has some history that is not necessarily negative, a blue "H"will appear in the header. A green "C" indicates that the case has citing references, but no direct or negative indirect history.

5.   Now, KeyCite the same opinion from Questions 3 and 4 by clicking on the flag in the document header. You should be using the **KC History** tab. What is the name of the 2002 Illinois case that "declined to extend by?"

6.   To view the sources that have cited your case, click on **KC Citing Ref.** What is the name of the August 2002 Illinois Appellate case that mentions your case?

7.   Click on **Limit Citing Refs**. You can limit citing references by headnote, locate term, jurisdiction, date, document type, or depth of treatment. Click on document type and locate law review articles. How many articles are listed?

8.   You can limit KeyCite to display only the cases that from a specific jurisdiction. Limit KeyCite to the cases from Missouri. Make sure you check **Doc Type - Other Courts**. What is the name of the 2002 Missouri case?

Cancel the limits by clicking on the Cancel Limits link. If necessary, return to the spilt-page view by clicking on the Spilt-Page View icon.

9.   Select the **Table of Authorities** by clicking on the **TOA** tab. Table of Authorities lists the cases cited **in** your case and enables you to see if any of the cases your case relied on have significant negative history. Click on the **TOA** tab for the *Hills* case decided in 2000. How many cases were cited in your case?

10. Next you will use the **Find** service. You can find a document by citation or title. Select the **Find** link from the toolbar. Retrieve the case at 118 S. Ct. 1. State the name of the case.

11. You can also find a document by its title. Click on **Find**, then on the link **Find by Title**. Click on **State Courts** and select **Connecticut** from the drop down box. Locate a Connecticut case titled *Jackson v. Johnson* dated Dec. 16, 1986. What is the volume and page number of the citation?

12. To begin a new search in a database, go to the Westlaw Directory by selecting the **Directory** link from the toolbar. Select **Georgia state** cases. Locate all of the cases involving the Georgia attorney Deborah A. Edwards. To restrict a search to the attorney field, click on the **arrow** icon before "Fields." What is the field abbreviation to locate an attorney?

13. Type in the attorney's name in the attorney field box. Locate cases involving Deborah A. Edwards. How many cases are displayed?

14. To display a specific case in the citation list in the left frame, click on the name of the case in the list. Click on the case decided November 29, 1990. State the plaintiff's **first** and **last** name.

15. To begin a new search in a different database, select the **Directory** link. In the **Search these databases** box in the Database Directory frame on the left, type in the federal database **CTA7** and click **GO**. To view a detailed description of a database, click on the Scope icon **"i."** What is in the CTA7 database?

16. KeySearch is a research tool that helps you find cases and secondary sources within a specific area of the law. KeySearch guides you through the selection of terms from a classification system based on the West Key Number System and then uses the key numbers and their underlying concepts to formulate a query for you. Click **KeySearch** on the toolbar. Locate cases with headnotes from South Carolina on nursing home license revocation. Click on Health - Nursing Homes - License revocation. Under **Choose a source**, make sure **Cases with West Headnotes** is selected. Then select **South Carolina State** cases from the drop down box. Make sure you check the box before this selection. What is the name of a 1988 case?

The **Research Trail** automatically creates a record of tasks you complete during a research session. You may want to view the trail, deliver the trail via email, download it, or print it. Remember to sign off WESTLAW by clicking **Sign Off**.

ASSIGNMENT SEVENTEEN
WESTLAW – PART TWO

GOALS OF THIS ASSIGNMENT:

To give you practice at formulating effective search strategies for researching statutes, regulations, secondary materials, and non-legal materials.

To introduce you to FIND, terms and connectors searching, natural language searching, and field searching.

This assignment was designed to be completed using WESTLAW on the Internet at http://lawschool.westlaw.com. **Refer to Rule 18.1 on Commercial Databases in** *The Bluebook*. **Sign onto WESTLAW.**

1. When you know a statute's citation, FIND is the easiest method for retrieving the statute. You need not enter a database; you can simply click on **Find** and you are in **Find a Document**. Type a citation into the **Enter Citation** box and click **GO**. You want to find Ind. Code Ann. § 3-3-3-3. Type **In. St. 3-3-3-3** into the **Enter Citation** box and click **GO**. What is the topic of this section?

2. To leave your found document and return to the database directory, select the **Directory** link on the toolbar. The **Find a Database Wizard** will walk you through the process of selecting a database that meets your research needs. The **Find a Database Wizard** is available from the Directory page. Locate the database for the Mo. Ann. Stat. What is the database identifier? Click on the Scope icon **"i"** to see the database identifier.

3. Click on **MO-ST-ANN**. Locate a statute designating the date for Arbor Day. State the citation according to *Bluebook* Rule 18.1.2.

4. To begin a new search in a new database, select the **Directory** link from the toolbar. Type **TN-ST**, the Tennessee unannotated statutes database, in the **Search these databases** box and click **GO**. You can limit your search to a specific field. To see which fields are available in this database choose the Terms and Connectors search method and click the **Scope i icon**. Then click on the **Searching and Fields** link. Scroll down toward the bottom of the scope document. You will see a list of the fields and their definitions. What material is included in the caption of a statute?

Click twice on your browser's Back button to go back to the TN-ST database query page.

5. Now, use the caption field to search. Locate a statute from Tennessee on rules on wagering by using the caption field. State the statute citation.

6. In statutory documents, you can view consecutive statutes. Click on the drop-down arrow of the box in the lower right-hand corner of the screen that says **"Locate."** Then click on **Docs in Seq** and click **GO**. WESTLAW automatically displays the next statute in sequence after your original statute. You can move either forward by clicking on the **LEFT** arrow at the bottom or backward by clicking on the **RIGHT** arrow at the bottom of the screen. Click on the **LEFT** arrow in the left frame to get back to your original statute from Question 5. Click on the **LEFT** arrow twice to get to the statute that precedes your original statute by two. State the section number for that statute and the title of that section.

7. We now want to conduct a search in the U.S.C. Access the U.S.C. database by clicking on the **Directory** link at the top of the page. Type **USC** in the **Search these databases** box and click **GO**. Locate a federal statute which established West Point.

8.   To retrieve federal regulations, access the Code of Federal Regulations (CFR) database by clicking on the **Directory**. Type **CFR** in the **Search these databases** box and click **GO**. Locate the regulation that lists salmon in the Columbia River Basin as an endangered species.

9.   Any final regulations published in the *Federal Register* that were issued after the latest C.F.R. database revision will be displayed automatically. Are there any new regulations from your answer to Question 8? If so, list the citations.

10.   You can search either the full text of legal periodicals on WESTLAW or the various indexes to legal periodicals. The *Legal Resource Index* database (LRI) includes all material covered in the *Current Law Index*. Access the LRI database by clicking the **Directory** link at the top of the page. Type **LRI** in the **Search these databases** and click **GO**. Locate articles on defective tire rims. State the citation of the article that appeared in the 1991 issue of *Trial*.

11.   Natural Language searching on WESTLAW allows you to search using standard English instead of terms and connectors. To change to Natural Language, select **Edit Search** from the drop-down list in the left frame and click **GO**. Now click on **Natural Language**. Use the same fact situation from Question 10 and type your search. Did you find the same 1991 law review article from *Trial*?

12.   Next, click on **Directory**, then **Westnews (News and Business Databases)**. Click
       on **Westnews: Complete Alphabetical List** then **Databases beginning with B**.
       Is the *Baltimore Sun* included in Westnews?

13.   Click on **Baltimore Sun (BALTSUN)**. Click on the arrow icon before "**Fields**" to
       bring up the **Field Restrictions** template. Locate a 2002 article in the Baltimore
       Sun written by Liz Atwood that discusses an ice cream mixer. What is the exact
       date of the article?

14.   The West Legal Directory database (WLD) contains information on attorneys,
       courts, judges, and judicial clerkships. To access the West Legal Directory, click
       the **Directory** link, then **Directories and Reference Materials** then **West Legal
       Directories (West Group)** and finally **West Legal Directory**. Locate Stephen
       Kelly in Peoria, Illinois by using the template. What is the name of his firm?

       The **Research Trail** automatically creates a record of tasks you complete during a
       research session. You may want to view the trail, deliver the trail via email,
       download it, or print it. Remember to sign off WESTLAW by clicking **Sign Off**.

ASSIGNMENT EIGHTEEN
LEXIS -- PART ONE

GOALS OF THIS ASSIGNMENT:
To give you practice at subject searches in case law and other sources.
To introduce you to Shepard's, Search Advisor, and Get a Document.

Answer Question 1 before you begin your research on LEXIS. Refer to *Understanding Lexis.com* or other reference material. Refer to Rule 18.1 on Commercial Electronic Databases in *The Bluebook*.

Assume that you are looking for state cases on the following fact situation. You are an attorney representing the driver of an automobile who was involved in a nighttime collision at an intersection where the traffic signals were not working due to a power outage. She wants to know what duty of care is required at an intersection with an inoperative traffic light.

1. Write out the search using terms and choosing connectors.

Use LEXIS on the Internet at http://www.lexisnexis.com/lawschool/

2. Find the relevant Court of Appeals of Washington case decided in 2001 and reported in the *Pacific Reporter*. Click on **Search - State Legal - U.S. - WA State Cases, Combined**. State the full citation of the case using the *Bluebook* citation format - Rule 10.

3. What do you click on to view the document quickly to see if it is on point?

4. If you click on Custom viewing, how would you view the case?

5. The **FOCUS** feature narrows your search to additional highlight words within the case. Click on **FOCUS**. Is the case, *Whitchurch v. McBride*, cited in your case?

6. On what page of the *Pacific Reporter* is this case discussed? Look for the page number preceded by **.

7. The Natural Language feature on LEXIS allows you to search in plain English, rather than using connectors. Click on **Search.** Choose from your last 20 sources - **WA State Cases, Combined**. To change to Natural Language, click on **Natural Language**. Use the same fact situation from Question 1 and type your search. Did you find the same 2001 Court of Appeals of Washington case? Make sure you locate the case published in P.3d.

8. In your case, you will notice core terms and core concepts. What are core concepts?

9. You already know that Shepard's offers full treatment and history analysis needed to verify the status of a case. Additionally, Shepard's provides you with a list of documents related to the issue that you are researching. Shepardize this 2001 Washington case by clicking on the **Shepard's signal** at the top of the case. What does the signal mean?

10. Examine the Shepard's display. How do you get specific citations that meet your research needs?

11. Click on **Custom Restrictions** at the top of the screen. Click the box for dissenting opinions (**Dissenting Op.**). State the name of the case whose dissenting opinion cites your case.

12. Click on the case from Question 11. Did this case also involve an intersection collision?

13. You can also Shepardize by clicking on **Shepard's®- Check a Citation**. Shepardize 196 F.3d 900. What does the Shepard's symbol indicate?

14.   From the citations listed in the results obtained in Question 13, what is the name of the opinion that has criticized your case?

15.   You can also begin your research by clicking on **Search Advisor**. Find family law cases on nonparental custody statutes.   Click on **Family Law**, click on **Child Custody**, click on **Awards**, then choose **State Family Law Cases** from the **Select Jurisdiction** drop down menu. Type your search request as a terms and connectors search.   How many cases are on the topic?

16.   You can also start with a particular citation to a case, a statute, or a law review article.   Click on **Get a Document** - then click on the **Citation** tab.   You are looking for the full text of a case, so click the **Full Text** button. Type 643 N.W.2d 359.   What is the name of the case?

17.   You can also get a case by its name.   Click on **Get a Document** tab.   Click on the **Party Name** tab.   Type Zadvydas and Davis in the windows.   Then click **U.S. Courts of Appeals** and select **5ᵗʰ Circuit** from the drop down menu.   Click on **Search**.   What is the F.3d citation of this case?

18.   Lastly, you can retrieve a case by its docket number.   Click on **Get a Document**, then the **Docket Number** tab.   Type 98-8384 and click on **US Supreme Court**. What is the name of the case?

Sign off LEXIS.

ASSIGNMENT NINETEEN
LEXIS -- PART TWO

GOAL OF THIS ASSIGNMENT:
To give you practice at formulating effective search strategies for researching statutes, regulations, and secondary materials on LEXIS.

This assignment was designed to be completed using LEXIS at http://www.lexisnexis.com/lawschool/. Refer to Rule 18.1 on Commercial Electronic Databases in *The Bluebook*.

1. When you know a statute's citation and want to retrieve its text, you should use **Get a Document.** You need not enter a database, you can simply type a citation into **Get a Document.** Click on **Get a Document**, click on the **Citation** tab. You want to find Mont. Code Ann. § 26-1-803 (2002). Type the citation. What is the topic of the section?

2. **Book Browse** allows you to view preceding and succeeding code sections of the statute without constructing another search request. Click on **Book Browse** located at the top of the screen. Using the citation from Question 1, what is the section number of the previous section?

3. Next locate a statute on medical power of attorney in the Texas database. To leave your found document and return to the sources screen, select **Search**. Use **Sources** and click on **States Legal - U.S.** Next click on **Texas,** then **Statutes & Regulations.** Finally click on **TX- Texas Statutes and Codes.** What is the citation of the statute that indicates the form for the medical power of attorney? Type your search terms. State the citation according to *The Bluebook*.

4. How many treatises and analytical materials are listed?

5. To begin a new search in a different database, click on **Search** in the left hand corner of the screen. Under **Look for a Source,** click on the **Find a Source** tab. In the box, type **United States Code Service**. In the **Find a Source Results**, click on **United States Code Service - Titles 1 through 50**. Search for the federal law that mandates that the Director of the Patent and Trademark Office maintain a library of scientific and other works and periodicals, both foreign and domestic.

6. Next use the Minnesota database to search the Minnesota Statutes.. Click **Search**. Under **Look for a Source**, click on the **Find a Source** tab. In the box, type **Minnesota Statutes**. In the **Find a Source Results**, select **MN - Minnesota Statutes**. Locate the statute that addresses the immunity from liability of a school bus driver under the Good Samaritan laws.

7. To retrieve federal regulations, access the Code of Federal Regulations (C.F.R.) database by first clicking on **Search,** then **Look for a Source**, then **Find a Source**. In the search box, type **CFR**. Select **CFR - Code of Federal Regulations** from the **Find a Source Results**. Locate the regulation that states financial assistance is the purpose of the early intervention program for infants and toddlers with disabilities.

8. Any final regulations published in the *Federal Register* that were issued after the latest C.F.R. database revision will be displayed automatically. How current is the section?

9. Use the C.F.R. section from Question 7 to use the FOCUS feature. The FOCUS feature allows you to highlight additional words within a document. Click on **FOCUS** and type **minority**. Does this term appear in this C.F.R. section?

10. Now go to the *Arkansas Democrat-Gazette* newspaper file. Click on **Search**. Then under the **Source** tab and **Look for a Source**, click on **Find a Source**. In the search box, type **Arkansas Democrat-Gazette** and select it from the **Find a Source Results**. Run a search using Document Segments by using the Terms and Connectors search. Segments are divisions or sections within a document. Segments can help to narrow your research by retrieving documents with relevant information in certain areas of the documents. Look for an article on inductees into the Boys and Girls Club Hall of Fame by Raschke. Byline is one of the segments. In the **Enter Search Terms** box, enter the first part of your search. Now add the byline segment. Click on **Restrict Search Using Document Segments.** In the first pull-down box, select your connector. In the next pull-down box, select your segment **BYLINE**. In the next box, type **Raschke**. What is the date of the article?

11. For this question, you will be looking for a law review article. Click on **Search**. Under **Look for a Source**, click on the **Find a Source** tab. In the search box, type **Law Reviews**. Select **Law Reviews Combined** from the **Find a Source Results**. Find an article that appeared in 1999 or 2000 on parallel litigation that was published in the *Baylor Law Review*.

12. Natural Language searching on LEXIS allows you to search using standard English instead of terms and connectors. To change to Natural Language, click on **Natural Language**. Use the same fact situation from Question 11 and type your search. Did you find the same 2000 article from the *Baylor Law Review*?

13. Martindale-Hubbell Law Directory is available on LEXIS. Click on **Search**. Under **Look for a Source**, click on the **Find a Source** tab. In the search box, type **Martindale-Hubbell Law Directory California**. Locate California attorney Mark Theodore. Remember to switch back to Terms and Connectors searching. Use the **NAME** segment. Where did Mark Theodore attend law school?

Sign off LEXIS.